SHOULD TREATMENT BE TERMINATED?

SHOULD
TREATMENT
BE
TERMINATED?

THOMAS C. ODEN

HARPER & ROW, PUBLISHERS

New York, Hagerstown, San Francisco, London

FIRST EDITION

Library of Congress Cataloging in Publication Data

Oden, Thomas C
   Should treatment be terminated?
     1. Terminal care. 2. Medical ethics. 3. Death.
I. Title.
R726.8.033   174′.2   76-9970
ISBN 0-06-066345-6

To my mother and father in memory of G. G.,

and to Jan and all the Pokornys in memory of Art

CONTENTS

PREFACE

The family is called into the hospital waiting room. The physician quietly and sensitively communicates the gravity of the situation. Successful treatment appears virtually hopeless. The family is confronted with several alternatives: long-term intensive care, or continued temporary life support but without intensive treatment of new complications, or the discontinuance of respiration which would allow the patient to die.

The family then tries to discern with each other and with their physician and clergy whether to withhold life-sustaining treatment. This book seeks to serve as a significant background or immediate resource for addressing this and related questions. It hopes to be sufficiently in touch with the family's dilemma that it may speak credibly to the tender moral conscience of a caring family sensitized by the irreversible illness of a loved one. And yet it also seeks to be sufficiently well-informed concerning the legal and medical options that it may serve as reliable guide amid the complexities of end-care decisions.

If you are in or close to the family of one critically ill, then you may be a part of a process of facing a life-death decision. You may be drawn into it even against your preference. If you are next of kin or near next of kin you may have to make a judgment about when to stop seemingly heroic treatment, whether new infections are to be treated, whether high-caloric feeding should continue, whether the patient should be told about his or her condition, whether to sign surgery permissions or documents that would provide organ donations in the event of death, or whether to provide extended care at home or in the hospital. You may also have to do some caring for disturbed members of the family. You may be involuntarily drawn into this web of critical decision making where mistakes in moral judgment are not easily back-tracked. This book offers you some practical guidance in negotiating these decisions.

The following two-column comparison displays two competing trends of end-care reasoning. The first column sets forth factors many think should make treatment termination acceptable. The second column raises doubts and objections.

SHOULD TREATMENT BE TERMINATED?

YES, IF	NO, BECAUSE
Yes, if there is informed consent of all relevant parties (patient, physician, hospital and family).	No. All parties conceivably could agree to an unjust or unwise termination; if, for example, there were only limited physical impairment such as hearing loss, that would not justify discontinuance even if all parties consented. So although consent is important, it does not stand alone as an absolute indicator of discontinuation.
Yes, if there is a permanent loss of all cognitive function,	No. There is always the possibility of misdiagnosis

YES, IF

NO, BECAUSE

all ability to understand; when the family and attending physicians agree there is no hope of regaining the capacity to think or experience normal human consciousness.

("It's happened before"— citing cases). Prognosis, the prediction of the future of the illness, is a notoriously inexact science. Besides, if you terminate "low quality of life" patients, where do you draw the line? Would not senile, retarded and genetically handicapped patients be endangered by the same rule?

Yes, if there is "irrefutable evidence that biological death is imminent" (AMA. House of Delegates Declaration).

No. Imminence of death is a tricky, variable, predictive calculation that would differ from physician to physician. Anyway, does it mean hours or days? The simple fact that death is near would not, by itself alone, justify termination of treatment in every case. You would not, for example, withhold respiration from a fully conscious dying patient who wishes to remain conscious.

Yes, if there is great suffering, or unrelievable pain.

No. Medications can relieve the pain. Counseling and supportive therapies can help with mental anguish. In the

YES, IF

NO, BECAUSE

Western religious experience, suffering is understood as a potential means of special grace and spiritual learning. Further, if suffering justifies the ending of life, then obviously suicide is morally acceptable. This cannot be.

Yes, if there is a lack of the will to live, total demoralization, or wishing for death.

No. Every doctor knows that some patients face periods of demoralization and depression. The patient's judgment is not always in his or her best interests during such low periods. The physician's duty extends to protecting the patient from the misjudgments of his own depression.

Yes, if continued hopeless treatment involves unconscionable cost to the family or society; if it places grave burdens such as potential impoverishment on those who care for the hopelessly dying.

No. For at what point does the value of life become a budget item? Anyway, most cases are covered by insurance arrangements, which should be humanized in the light of newer life-sustaining technologies.

Yes, if there is an immediate limited availability of life-

No. In most cases nearby medical facilities are available

YES, IF

NO, BECAUSE

sustaining equipment or heavy stress on intensive care facilities. This situation is similar to the procedure of triage, where combat casualties are divided into hopeless cases who get no medical attention, and more hopeful cases who receive medical attention.

in crises. Anyway, triage is an ethic of exceptions under emergency conditions of warfare. You cannot build a general set of normal guidelines on exceptions.

Yes, if the next of kin are unwilling to provide long-term care for a hopelessly ill patient.

No. The value of that patient's life does not depend, according to law and common moral decency, on whether his relatives are willing to care for him.

This book seeks to draw together the best of both sides of the above arguments and to reject the excess of both. These arguments show that it is impossible to answer the questions of treatment termination with a simple yes or no. It requires deeper exploration into specific contingencies and details.

What follows is mainly addressed to the family of the seriously ill person. Its purpose is to set forth reliable guidelines on when, how and why active treatment may legitimately be ended or extended. It may also serve as a moral advisory for medical professionals, hospital ethics committees, attorneys, pastors and chaplains, as well as legislators considering treatment refusal questions or judges asked to decide guardianship questions. In addition to these readers, I sincerely hope that it might be of practical value to the patient as well, or to anyone who is thinking of signing a treatment refusal document in advance of serious illness.

This brings us to our first guideline: *Persons who are asked to give informed consent to treatment discontinuance have moral obligation to be informed.* You may need to be informed not only about the medical condition of the patient, but also on the ethical principles that should govern a judgment to extend or end life. Thus this book.

The situation with which the family has to deal will be largely unique in its details. No book can anticipate all the factors that will be involved in a specific case. Hence it is impossible to set down exhaustive rules on what should be done in every conceivable situation. Sometimes it is right to continue heroic treatment at incalculable cost. In some circumstances, which we will carefully specify, it is appropriate, though always regrettable, to withhold new medical initiatives on emergencies and infections so as to allow irreversible illness to take its course. The judgment as to which alternative is appropriate in a particular set of circumstances will emerge from considering the situation itself in all its complexities against a series of principles or guidelines. This book sets forth some forty-two guidelines to questions as diverse as whether to consent to hospitalization and how heavily should the severity of discomfort be weighed.

Forty-two guidelines! Must the moral analysis of these matters be that complex? Not, of course, in all situations. Not every guideline will have to be considered in every case. Hopefully each guideline will be seen in its correlation with all others, not as if any one were separable from a larger unified pattern of moral reasoning. None is absolutely required in every situation, and yet any one will be found to be clearly required in some situations. The wisdom required to select which guideline is appropriate to which situation is itself a crucial part of the capacity for moral reasoning which this discussion would hope to nurture.

No simplistic formula, no predisposed set of mind, no point of view with a predetermined answer to be routinely applied, can adequately meet the crisis of the family in the waiting room. A rigid formula that advises, "Keep every patient alive at all costs," is no more adequate than the thoughtless collusion to end the life of another with an easy conscience as if the decision were purely a matter of individual freedom without reference to social responsibility or any transcendent obligation to the source of life.

In November 1975 a nationwide poll by the William Hamilton Organization asked: "Suppose a person is in the hospital and, according to all medical evidence, is dying and cannot be cured or saved. Do you feel that it would be right to simply let that person die or should every effort be made to keep him alive?" Fifty-nine percent said let such a person die. Thirty percent said every effort should be made to keep the person alive. The remainder were undecided. A 1976 NBC poll asked: "Should doctors use mechanical means to keep patients alive if there is no chance to recover?" Seventy-two percent answered no, 16 percent yes and 12 percent were undecided. Polls such as this make the regrettable mistake of reducing an intricate set of issues to their least meaningful level of generalization. For what if the patient is a young father of four who is dying and definitely cannot be cured, but still has a life expectancy of two years, is fully lucid, has a strong will to live, and is not in any pain. No reasonable person knowing those particular facts would responsibly say that life-support medicine should be withheld, merely because the condition is irreversible. This is the grievous limitation of all the polls I have seen: they leave out most of the relevant details upon which one might make a clear-headed judgment.

We will thread our way through these specifics. The medical practitioner works relentlessly to save life, but if life cannot be saved, when is it required or permitted to not prolong unnecessary suffering? When is it a duty to allow natural causes to relieve suffering by death? Beyond the normal life-preserving obligation, can the physician legally and morally omit a treatment he knows would prolong life, or discontinue a treatment currently sustaining life? Is the right to self-determination absolute, or to what degree limited? Is there anything a person can or should do prior to becoming ill that may decrease the chance of having his wishes overridden by a strong legal tradition which favors preservation of life even under conditions of suffering?

We are prone to imagine that these questions are totally new and unprecedented, due to the recent achievements of medical technology in extending life; but the premortem questions that trouble us most deeply are hardly new. It is a common illusion of the modern mind that all our moral quandaries today are unprecedented. Weren't the feelings of anticipatory grief that the Stone Age father would have felt in the presence of his dying child essentially the same as those we may feel today? When the patient of a medieval physician begged to die during a plague to shorten his period of suffering, didn't he place the physician in the same quandary as does the modern patient who raises that same question amid improved technologies? Herbs for ending life were available in ancient Greece. The same moral questions confronted persons then who had the capacity to end life as today. The inestimable value of life has not changed. The duty to relieve suffering has not changed. Whenever the duty to relieve suffering has clashed with the value of life itself, the essential issues have been the same as those we face today. Technology itself has not fundamentally changed these perennial moral dilemmas.

But on what grounds does any one author presume to offer insights that necessarily must emerge from several disciplines— law, medicine and ethics? By vocation, I teach theology and ethics in a Protestant theological seminary. In a previous book, *After Therapy What?*, I explored with an interdisciplinary team of scholars the troublesome dilemmas concerning when psychotherapeutic treatment should be terminated. A postdoctoral year spent studying with the medical faculty at Heidelberg, Germany, and another period of study at the Texas Medical Center in Houston, have allowed me to pursue questions of medical ethics in a medical setting. But this "expertise" cannot claim too much. For among the several books I have written, this is by far the most difficult, challenging, and resistant to oversimplification. I have found no easy answers to the questions of easy death.

Robert Glaser has written: "At this point in medical history, where we can look forward to further developments and perfection of life-prolonging measures, we must attempt to define in more specific ways the criteria for their employment, and particularly the criteria for their discontinuation." The family of a terminally ill patient knows in the agony of direct experience the throbbing urgency of Glaser's observation.

The Drew University Interdisciplinary Study of Treatment Termination, which I was privileged to convene and chair, generated some scientific and statistical evidence that will help us define these criteria. This study identified the variable factors at work in treatment discontinuation decisions and showed their relative weight. This book builds on that evidence and seeks to develop clear and reliable moral guidelines for treatment discontinuance.

I wish to acknowledge my continuing indebtedness to all who so creatively participated in that study: physicians Henry Liss, Joseph Fennelly, and Robert Francis, attorney Joseph Imbriaco, Bruce Hilton of the National Center for Bio-Ethics, and to my colleagues Neal Riemer, James J. Nagle, Donald G. Jones, and Chaplain Randolph L. Jones. To Paul Hardin, not only as my chief administrative officer, but more so as friend and imaginative partner in dialogue, I express my special thanks. To Philip K. Jensen, James M. O'Kane, Thomas Makosky, Richard A. Detweiler, and John Hall I am grateful for patient assistance in designing our computer program. Portions of the ensuing argument have appeared in articles in Hastings Center Report, the National Observer, and the Christian Century. Illuminating discussions with such perceptive ethics colleagues as Paul Ramsey, Leo Farley, Kenneth Vaux, Edward LeRoy Long, Jr., Charles West, Will

Herberg, and George Kelsey have shaped this discussion, and even though none of its defects should be in any way attributed to them, I am grateful for their prudent and helpful dialogue.

Finally, I owe to three persons in particular, my mother, father, and sister-in-law to whom this book is affectionately dedicated, a set of memories of what it means to care empathically, even at considerable cost, for a seriously ill person for a very long time, and to grow magnificently through the process as a person and as a covenant partner. For the last fifteen of my grandmother's ninety-four years, my remarkable parents cared for her through numerous crises, loss of hearing, loss of mobility, and loss of physical capacities, but not the loss of her will to affirm and receive life under its specific conditions of limitation. Jan Pokorny took care of her husband Art through a very rough terminal illness that required the best of her judgment, courage, insight, and perseverance. These three people have shown me what it means to value life even in the midst of its steady and inexorable deterioration, without losing either faith or realism, but committed above all to serve and care for the person with whom they were bound in covenant companionship. I hope I can express here even a fraction of the insight and courage they had in their end-care judgments.

Drew Forest
Madison, N.J.

INTRODUCTION: THE DILEMMAS OF LIFE SUPPORT

Ethical reflection begins at the point of our trying to provide reasons to ourselves and others as to why certain actions are considered right or wrong. The simplest way initially to exercise our capacity for ethical reflection amid serious illness is to look at several cases and try to decide what we would do in those instances, seeking to sort out the reasons why we made those judgments.

Each of the following cases contains seven elements that belong to the consideration of any case of serious illness:

- Age, marital status and general information about the patient
- Severity of physical impairment
- Probable life expectancy
- Severity of impaired understanding
- Degree of discomfort
- The patient's treatment preference, if conscious
- The family's treatment preferences

You may find it useful and challenging to rank order these seven factors in each case in the order of their importance to you in arriving at your decision.

1

• Tony Sanchez is an eighteen-year-old son of a welfare re-
cipient. • A serious accident has left him as a quadriplegic
(unable to use his arms and legs) requiring a great deal of hospital care. In addition, however, he has recently developed a
serious cardiac malfunction which will require immediate resuscitation and probably a long series of surgeries with periodic
intensive care. • If resuscitated and treated actively, his life
expectancy is probably many years. If not resuscitated, he will die
immediately. • The accident left him with no serious cognitive impairment. The nurses have come to know him as a warm,
sensitive, life-affirming, beautiful person. • As to his probable
discomfort level if treated, past evidence indicates that he has ad-
justed well to the severe limitations of his quadriplegic condition,
and his strong will to live leads one to believe that he would ad-
just also to further incapacities. • Since he is currently unconscious, his consent to treatment is not possible to ascertain.
• Although his mother has serious reservations about her ability
to provide even a small fraction of his medical costs and only
a small portion of time in caring for him, she is willing to follow
the physician's advice of either treatment continuance or discontinuance. Would you resuscitate and treat actively, or not
resuscitate?

• Charles Martin is a sixty-six-year-old retired carpenter, married, with four children and nine grandchildren. • Now hospitalized, he is experiencing acute kidney failure that will require
regular dialysis three times per week for the remainder of his life.
• Although temporarily immobilizing and at times painful, this
treatment is expected to be successful, with a probable life expectancy of two to five years. • He is fully conscious and capable
of communicating effectively. • Currently he is experiencing
extreme frustrations amid the inconveniences of the conditions of
hospitalization necessary for his survival. • Following a sleep-
less night, he has just expressed his treatment preference: He

wishes to go home and die. He is, at this point, tired of struggling with suffering and dreads future treatment routines. He prefers pain medication only, but without any attempt to treat the renal failure that will soon take his life without dialysis. • His wife and children, however, have a strong conviction that he should proceed with dialysis, as his physician recommends, since it is generally considered to be a successful treatment. Both physician and family agree that he is temporarily in a period of depression that will later be overcome with continued active treatment. As a friend of Charles Martin and his family, would you, on the basis of this information, help facilitate a decision to continue active treatment or to take the patient home and acquiesce to the disease?

• Nancy Jefferson is a fifty-six-year-old, black mother of two grown children who has for many years worked as an elevator operator in a local office building. • A stroke has left her with a severe and probably permanent loss of the capacity to speak. • Although she will require convalescent care for the remainder of her life, she is expected to live five to ten years. • Her ability to understand others communicating to her is unimpaired, and she is able to respond nonverbally to others' feelings and expressions. • Despite occasional discomfort, she is experiencing no mental anguish or despair. • Treatment preferences have not been discussed with the patient, although her will to live apparently remains strong. • The patient recently, however, has contracted a critical virus infection. When the doctor expressed the seriousness of this infection to the family, it became apparent that their treatment preference was to not vigorously treat the new infection so as to allow death very possibly to occur, since they have felt heavily burdened by the thought of a prolonged convalescence. They have gone so far, in fact, as to withhold their consent to hospitalization.

As a friend of Nancy Jefferson and her family, would you help encourage a decision in the direction of treatment or nontreatment of the infection? Rank order the seven factors in terms of the weight that each has in your mind as you weigh the decision.

• James Morganthau is a forty-three-year-old brickmason, married with two children, whom the community has come to know well as a volunteer coach of Little League baseball. • With injuries sustained in an automobile accident, Mr. Morganthau requires immediate surgery and blood transfusions without which his life cannot be sustained. He has serious lacerations and internal damage, the full extent of which is unknown. At present his breathing is being assisted by a mechanical respirator, but with successful surgery, that would not need to be continued. • His life expectancy is, with surgery, many years, but almost immediate death without it. • Although now in a coma, it is considered probable that he will recover all cognitive functions. • Since he is currently not conscious, he is not experiencing any pain. • The patient is a committed Jehovah's Witness, and is, according to the testimony of his family, a firm believer in that faith's view that blood transfusions are against God's law and moral law. So the family has indicated to the physicians that the patient would prefer nontreatment if it requires blood transfusion. • The family are also devout Jehovah's Witnesses, and object to the transfusion.

You have been consulted by a physician friend as to whether you think the hospital should seek temporary guardianship of the patient on an emergency basis and perform the surgery including transfusion which apparently is required to sustain the person's life. Would you advise getting the court order and proceeding with surgery, or allowing the patient to die?

• Eunice Grant is a sixty-three-year-old head librarian, unmarried but with two sisters and numerous nieces and nephews. Wise investments have allowed her to accumulate considerable property and she is known to be very heavily insured. • She is currently hospitalized with a chronic genitourinary ailment which will require continued convalescent care following her discharge from the hospital. • Despite a loss of mobility from this incapacitation, and considerable discomfort, she is given a heartening long-range prognosis of several more years life expectancy with good medical care. • This illness does not adversely affect her ability to think, communicate, or understand in any way. • Although the pain medications are able to control her actual physical pain, she has an intense dread of invalidism. Furthermore she has a distinct distaste for the medical routines and perceived indignities of the conditions necessary to sustain her life. • Eunice Grant has signed a treatment-refusal document indicating her desire to not be treated under these conditions, which she mailed to her physician and attorney over a year ago. Her present attitude, however, wavers between an uncertain will to live and at times a severe depression over her condition. • Her family is aware of the treatment-refusal document, and prefer nontreatment, discounting those times when she appears to have some will to live. Some members of the family, in fact, are talking about malpractice litigation if the physician continues to pursue active treatment.

As a friend of Eunice Grant and her family, would you encourage continued active treatment or the withholding of active treatment? Having rank ordered these seven factors, ask yourself why the highest ranking factor was more important to you than the others.

• Nikos Constantinos is a thirty-six-year-old Cypriot political refugee and immigrant, married with one child, who has been working until recently as a kitchen helper in a local restaurant. • A mugging victim, he is currently on a respirator, experiencing complete and probably permanent loss of respiratory function. • His physicians have irrefutable evidence that biological death is imminent. • He has been in a comatose condition since he arrived at the hospital, two weeks ago. He does not, however, meet the Harvard criteria for brain death, since he registers continuing brain waves on the electroencephalograph machine. • Since he is deeply comatose, he has no conscious experience of discomfort at present. • His own treatment preference under these circumstances is unknown, but according to the testimony of his wife, he would prefer, if he could speak, to have treatment terminated. • The wife, her family, and friends unanimously agree. As a friend of Nikos Constantinos and his family, would you encourage them to continue respiration until his demise, or disconnect the respirator to allow his death? Having rank ordered these seven factors, ask yourself why you reasoned in the way you did.

• June Horton is a twenty-nine-year-old mother of two small children, and the wife of a surgeon. • For three years she has had an arrested case of leukemia, but now a crisis has arisen. She is in intensive care receiving chemotherapy, extremely weakened, struggling for her life. • The prognosis at best is three weeks to six months. • She has not lost any mental capacity, but the heavy medications have temporarily skewed her ability to communicate. • To the degree that she is conscious, she is experiencing considerable suffering. In periods of lucidity, she appears to be struggling hard for life. • Her own treatment preferences, however, have not been openly discussed. • Her husband (the surgeon) and her mother are determined that all viable forms of active treatment should continue. The remainder of her family, her father, and brothers, are all convinced that the medications are only prolonging her suffering, and that she should be allowed to die. As a close friend of June Horton, would you encourage the family to continue active chemotherapeutic and other treatment or to provide her only palliative treatment and acquiesce to the illness?

1. WHO DECIDES?

Who has the legal and moral right to make a life-terminating decision? The first step in answering this is to identify the extent and limits of the conscious patient's right to refuse treatment.

Patient Rights. Resentment against the physician's authority is likely to decrease as more patients learn of their own legitimate rights under law to withhold consent. Each time a conscious patient asks a physician to treat, the right to withhold consent to treatment is implied. The competent patient grants the physician the right to treat. The physician treats essentially by the permission of the patient, and always functions as an agent in service of the patient. Once granted, this permission is assumed to continue, unless specifically disavowed.

The lucid patient's rights are clearly spelled out by the American Hospital Association:

The patient has the right to obtain from his physician complete current information concerning his diagnosis, treatment, and prognosis in terms the patient can be reasonably expected to understand. . . . The patient has the right to receive from his physician information necessary to give informed consent, prior to the start of any procedure and/or treatment. Except in emergencies, such information for informed consent should include but not necessarily be limited to the specific procedure and/or treatment, the medically significant risks involved, and the probable duration of incapacitation. . . . The patient has the right to refuse treatment to the extent permitted by law.

As a competent patient suffering a nonterminal illness, you have an untrammelled right to decide whether to accept treatment or not. You can judge for yourself whether it is in your interest to take surgical risks, or to what extent you want to submit yourself to a rigorous hospitalization.

You have a right to refuse treatment "to the extent permitted by law." But what is the extent permitted by law? Does the law, for example, condone suicidal aggressions against one's own life? The right to treatment refusal does not invariably extend to the right voluntarily to refuse life-support systems currently in use, if for example, a mother of small children has a recoverable ailment and a reasonably long life expectancy. If we set aside such exceptions as severe depression and terminal emergencies, however, we can confidently formulate our second guideline: *You have a right to refuse treatment to the extent permitted by law if you are conscious and competent.*

My purpose now is to discuss some of these exceptions. These often have to do with situations where the patient will die if treatment is terminated. Here the state has traditionally expressed a compelling interest in the equal protection of life.

The Limits of Consent. There are good reasons to believe that in some situations when people are seriously ill, their good judgment tends to become temporarily distorted, skewed by the stresses of suffering. Guideline three: *Severe depression must be compensated for by the wise judgment of the sensitive physician and family, who may under conditions of critical illness know better how to protect the best interest of the seriously ill patient than does the patient himself.*

8   Should Treatment Be Terminated?

In serious illness the emotional state of the patient is often a crucial factor in recovery. There are moments of depression amid any major illness or surgery, as every physician knows, when the patient becomes demoralized. Obviously those providing medical care must not in these moments simply follow the temporary fevered wish of the depressed patient to end it all now. Thus there are times when physician and kin have a positive duty to the patient to prolong his life contrary to his wish and against his specific and even urgent request. This is the most obvious reason why patient consent is not an absolute indicator of treatment termination.

When asked whether a person has the right to take his or her own life during a terminal illness, or whether we have the right to prevent this act, Dr. Elisabeth Kübler-Ross wisely answered: "If a patient is deeply depressed and wants to end his life we must first try to help him out of this depression. . . . If he is pathologically depressed, I would regard it my duty as a psychiatrist to get him out of the depression. . . . If he signs himself out of the hospital and refuses to take medication, he has the right to do so. If the patient is not mentally ill, we have to allow him this decision. If he is mentally ill, I would naturally request a psychiatric consultation, and see if we can get him into a better emotional state to make this decision rationally and in accordance with his real wishes."

Concurrent Consensus. Despite the difficulty of hard choices, who finally must make the decision to continue or discontinue treatment of a terminally ill patient? Prior to the *Quinlan* case (1976) there was no legally sanctioned procedure for terminating treatment, although physicians throughout history have practiced "benign neglect" or "judicious neglect" of patients for whom further treatment was not meaningful. The *Quinlan* ruling, however, if followed by subsequent court decisions, gives us a clear procedure for obtaining consent to treatment termination without criminal liability.

Accordingly, there are four parties whose consent must concur if treatment is to be terminated with full guarantees of the patient's right to equal protection of his life under law:

- The patient's consent must be implied, and none of the other consenting parties can act legally to end life except on the basis of its being in the best interests of the patient.
- The family, guardian or immediate next to kin must consent if treatment is to be terminated, and if the family's consent is not unanimous or is seriously lacking in moral certainty, that presents a substantial obstacle to termination.
- The attending physicians must have come to a responsible conclusion that "there is no reasonable possibility of return to cognitive and sapient life" or a prognosis of some similar magnitude, or that "there is irrefutable evidence that biological death is imminent."
- If all these parties concur, then it is possible to proceed to consult with the hospital ethics committee, "composed of physicians, social workers, attorneys, and theologians, which serves to review the individual circumstances of ethical dilemma." This committee acts as a "safeguard for patients and their caretakers. Generally, the authority of these committees is primarily restricted to the hospital setting and their official status is more that of an advisory body than of an enforcing body." Their purpose is to explore "all of the options for a particular patient," and to "provide a regular forum for more input and dialogue in individual situations, and to allow the responsibility of these judgments to be shared." The *Quinlan* ruling compared the value of these committees to the value of "multijudge courts in finally resolving on appeal difficult questions of law."

In this way the court has sought to safeguard the lives of defenseless patients from "less than worthy motivations of family or physician." The *Quinlan* ruling did not require these four consenting parties, if they unanimously agreed to termination, to apply to a court to confirm their decision, but rather stated its confidence that "such decisions, thus determined to be in accordance with medical practice and prevailing standards, would be acceptable by society and by the courts."

By what criteria are these four consenting parties to decide to end life? That is the subject of a searching investigation in chapter 2. At present, we are speaking not of *how* these parties should weigh the variables of termination decisions, but rather at the more elementary level of *who* must finally give informed consent to treatment termination if it is to be surrounded with the constitutional guarantees of the equal protection of life under law.

Our fourth guideline answers the question of this chapter: Who Decides? *Four key consenting parties—implied patient consent, family consent, physician consent, and hospital ethics committee consent—must concur unanimously if active treatment is to be terminated in such a way as to guarantee the patient's legal right to life. Any lack of unanimity among these consenting parties is likely to force the question into the courts for judicial review.*

Must One Consent to Hospitalization? Since 75 percent of all premortem care occurs in hospitals, our discussion thus far has assumed that the dying patient is hospitalized under the care of a physician. But that is not always the case. For if the patient is not under the care of a licensed medical practitioner and is not hospitalized, then the patient and family simply must use their own best judgment about what is in the best interests of the patient. In that case, since no decision has been made to begin treatment, no decision is needed on whether to discontinue treatment.

Ironically, one radical way to insure that a preference for nontreatment will be respected is not to contract with the hospital in the first instance for treatment. "A dying person can hold almost complete control over how he lives his last days by not entering a hospital, or can regain it by leaving the hospital" (Glaser and Straus). "As a result, quite a few 'moribund' patients afterward stride out of the hospital in defiance." (Hendin). The decision not to enter a hospital, of course, may be a limiting decision for you, instead of an expansion of possibilities. If you have a compelling desire to be fully in control of your situation, however, and are extremely frustrated by the conditions of hospitalization, this is an alternative you may be forced to consider.

Do you have a right to refuse hospitalization? No law or moral constraint requires all patients under all circumstances to seek or consent to hospitalization when their lives are endangered. In most cases, however, charity to oneself and the natural desire for self-preservation would lead one reasonably to follow the advice of a physician should hospitalization be indicated.

Once having been admitted to a hospital and having given consent to hospitalization, it may actually be more difficult for you to withdraw that consent than it was initially to give it. For in the hospital you will be under medical surveillance, whereas if you decide against hospitalization, no such surveillance exists. Thus the next guideline is: *You should be aware that your consent to hospitalization places you in a frame of reference of general medical surveillance which may to some degree limit your freedom to withhold consent at some future time.*

Should a seriously ill fully conscious patient be allowed to go home on request if death is a near-term probability? I think so. I think the Patient's Rights Bill of the American Hospital Association guarantees that right, with one exception—when a court order has provided temporary guardianship to administer emergency or life-sustaining medical care to a patient whose interests the courts have judged to be endangered.

Guardianship. A nonlucid patient sharply intensifies the moral ambiguities of a termination decision. Then patient preference becomes a matter of speculation. Such a patient may be weakened temporarily by surgery or illness, doped by medication, or be unconscious during emergencies when consent is immediately required. He may be psychiatrically judged to be incompetent. He may be senile. He may be temporarily comatose, or at worst persistently comatose. These are the cases that have presented the greatest perplexities for the courts.

When a hospital patient becomes unconscious or incompetent, someone must act to protect his best interests. Guideline six: *Legal guardianship of an incompetent ordinarily falls to the next of kin, not as some assume to the physician.* The physician may assume implied consent in emergencies when no next of kin is available. But in a monumental decision such as termination of life support, the physician is not likely to act on his own.

In some borderline cases the medical practitioner may be uncertain as to whether the semiconscious patient is capable of exercising good discretion and informed consent. In such cases the tendency may be to consult the patient, but weigh heavily the opinions of the family or patient advocates as to what the probable preferences of the patient are likely to be.

Duties of the Guardian. If you as guardian are asked to make a life-extension or termination judgment for someone who is incompetent, this guideline should be scrupulously observed: *It is the guardian's duty to judge not what he, the guardian, would prefer under those circumstances, but what he sincerely thinks the patient would prefer under those circumstances, based on previous knowledge of the patient. If, however, the guardian has no explicit knowledge as to what the patient would prefer, then he may follow the golden rule (do unto others as you would have them do unto you) and judge how he would wish to be treated under those circumstances.* If there happen to be significant differences between the guardian's preferences and the patient's preferences, the guardian owes it to the patient to follow what he knows to be the patient's preference.

The more frequent guardianship conflicts occur, however, in cases where the family views the patient's best interests in a different way than the medical practitioners. If the physician or hospital have reason to believe that the family or guardian of an incompetent person is not acting strictly in the patient's best interests, they may petition a court for the appointment of a temporary guardian. The *Heston, Quinlan,* and other cases illustrate the entanglements resulting from these conflicts.

In January 1972 a seventy-nine-year-old New York man in a semicomatose condition needed for survival an operation for the replacement of a pacemaker. His wife, acting as guardian, refused permission for the surgery. The hospital then petitioned a court for the appointment of a temporary guardian to authorize the surgery. The court granted the request and ordered the hospital to "perform whatever medical and surgical procedures" were "necessary to protect or sustain the health or life" of the patient.

In October of 1973 a Long Island judge made a twenty-nine-day-old Downs Syndrome infant the temporary ward of a state social services agency after the parents refused permission for an operation necessary for survival. In February of 1974 a Maine judge ordered surgery allowing feeding of a severely deformed infant whose parents had refused treatment when physicians indicated that the infant would be severely impaired.

Should guardianship be granted to one who expressly wishes life-sustaining treatment to be terminated? There does remain some doubt as to whether the state can on the one hand protect the life of an incompetent person, and at the same time grant guardianship to one who knowingly would end the incompetent's life. Even the attorney who first developed the "living will" document has argued that guardians should not be permitted to make declarations for someone else that would terminate his life. The essence of the living will is that the person must speak for himself. The living will, therefore, does not apply to any case of involuntary treatment termination.

Some may regard the person near death as less sacrosanct and therefore closer to legitimizing treatment discontinuance than the person with a long life expectancy. But the law, in theory at least, judges these two persons exactly as equals. The law does not show less interest in protecting equally the life of the dying person than it does in protecting the healthy person. If anything, the law has shown a compensatory protectiveness toward those who cannot protect themselves. The defenseless, dying person, by this logic, especially and urgently deserves the equal protection of law.

A *Religious Right to Death*? Does the guardian's right to believe and practice religion include the freedom or right to expose the ward to death? All the case law is on the side of a negative answer (*Prince* v. *Mass., Heston, Quinlan*). Freedom of religion encompasses no right to cause death.

In the landmark case of *J.F.K. Memorial Hospital* v. *Heston* the hospital took action on a patient who was unconscious and required a blood transfusion. The patient and her mother, as sincere Jehovah's Witnesses, objected to blood transfusions on religious grounds. The hospital asked the Superior Court judge for guardianship at 1:30 A.M., which was granted, and the surgery and transfusion were successfully performed at 4:30 that same morning. The court found that even the clearly established religious beliefs of the patient were insufficient to overcome the state's paramount interest in the protection of life. The court concluded that "there is no constitutional right to choose to die."

Admittedly, one has an unfettered right to religious belief, without impediments, but religious practices are "not wholly immune from governmental restraint" (*Reynolds* v. *U.S.*). Justice Weintraub's classic example: Suppose you have a cult of human sacrifice. One has an absolute right to *believe* in human sacrifice, but not to *practice* it. The *Heston* ruling shapes our eighth guideline: ***The court can compel religiously rejected medical treatment to protect the life of an unconscious patient whose current consent is unknown.***

Should You Make a Living Will? Should you sign a treatment-refusal document specifying the conditions for termination? They are not all alike. Some ask for illegal acts. Some reject *all* artificial means, which would include pacemakers, oxygen, respiration, and broadly conceived, all medications, even such benign mechanical devices as hearing aids, if strictly interpreted. Most of them lean heavily on the concept of "no reasonable expectation of recovery," which is a debatable concept, and at best an uncertain probability estimate. Some treatment-refusal documents request the ending of life for any "permanent physical disability." This could include hearing loss or the loss of a toe. Some are so loosely written that they can be expected to have no legal and very little moral force. Almost all the above defects are found in one document alone, the Euthanasia Education Council's widely circulated "A Living Will."

Other treatment-refusal documents carelessly ask for the ending of life in "any condition requiring the use—beyond two weeks —of mechanical equipment for breathing, heart action, feeding, dialysis, or brain function without a prognosis of full recovery of my vital organs." The obvious problem is that it is virtually impossible for any physician to insure a prognosis of full recovery for any illness, much less one involving serious illness. This language would imply the rejection, for example, of a pacemaker, after two weeks, for heart ailments that may be easily correctable. It would not allow intravenous feeding beyond two weeks for "any condition" without virtually certain full recovery. It would not allow any treatment of renal failure, which is increasingly becoming more conveniently treatable with the improvement of portable dialysis machines. The same document requests the doctor to end a person's life if he or she is "deprived of independent mobility." Any signer who could not walk presumably would be discontinued, if such a document were scrupulously followed. Furthermore the life of anyone who was "unable to take care of my own bodily functions" would be ended.

16 Should Treatment Be Terminated?

Even more recklessly the same document asks for others to end the signer's life if he or she experiences "only partial consciousness" (don't faint if you sign this one), or "any other evidence of advanced senility," or "any progressive deterioration of muscle, bone, or tissue requiring an increasing dependence on intravenous substances." What would be done in the case of an arrested malignancy which still offered considerable time, perhaps years, of continued meaningful existence? The same document asks in advance for death in case of loss of vision so that one cannot read. It asks for death in case of total deafness. This is incredible. Yet such a foolish and impossibly generalized document is proposed as a model by one who is taken by some to be an expert on thanatology, Marya Mannes.

Dr. Milton Heifetz's "Directive to My Physician" also has serious limitations. It recklessly asserts an unqualified and "complete right of self-determination." In an uncertain legal environment in which malpractice is already a serious social predicament, Heifetz's directive accelerates the malpractice threat by aggressively throwing down the gauntlet: "If any action is taken contrary to these expressed demands, I hereby request my next of kin or legal representative to consider—and if necessary, to take —legal action against those involved."

So should you sign a living will? Not if it has these defects. All those I have seen have serious defects, but among these the better one is Dr. Heifetz's. My objection to treatment-refusal documents of all kinds I have seen is that they try unsuccessfully to anticipate extraordinarily complex contingencies. There are too many variables to anticipate and qualify them adequately. They are controlling rather than acquiescing documents. They want specifically to control all the conditions under which death occurs. Thus they tend to oversimplify the extremely variable conditions under which treatment theoretically would be terminated.

Finally, what conditions would prevail if one wrote a "living will" sincerely affirming the desire to withhold treatment and then in lucid moments of irreversible illness expressly changed one's mind? Under those circumstances the living will would be unenforceable and would have no persuasive power.

This is precisely the trouble the courts have found in the "living will" concept: it is hard to determine whether a previous expression of a life or death treatment preference is firmly held in the present. For it is always possible to revise one's convictions, especially when actually facing death. And once an action leading to death has been taken, there are no more remedies. Death itself is the most irreversible of all decisions.

Guideline nine: *The courts have found it difficult to establish the permanency of treatment-refusal convictions once for all, in advance, for all possible contingencies.* Even in the *Heston* case where there was a formally embraced and sincerely affirmed religious belief that death is preferable to a blood transfusion, the courts held that "the instinct for survival is the almost immutable law of self-preservation," which in critical situations "is to be followed rather than a previously stated disposition to die." The court held in the *Osborne* case: "Where the patient is comatose, or suffering an impairment of capacity for choice, it may be better to give weight to the known instinct for survival, which can in a critical situation alter previous convictions. In such cases it cannot be determined with certainty that a deliberate and intelligent choice has been made."

If some of these defects can be overcome, however, treatment-refusal documents may come to play a limited but useful role in defining patient rights and interests amid the ambiguities of end-care hospitalization.

In 1912, a notorious case occurred. Mrs. Sarah Harris, a thirty-three-year-old paralytic mother of two begged the sanitarium officials of the state of New York to end her life. She refused to see her small children because she did not want them to be disturbed by her condition. In a heartrending letter to the newspapers she said: "There is not one thing on earth which could give me the faintest sensation of pleasure. . . . The one thing I can look forward to is death." Although her case was widely debated, her request was not granted. A year later a visiting physician met her, discussed her case history, and an operation was performed which relieved her of the intense pain. This brought about a complete change of attitude. She admitted that the doctor's certainty about her hopelessness was what caused her plea for mercy death. "When I asked for euthanasia I would have hailed it as a welcome deliverance," she said. "Now I shudder to think what might have happened had such a law been enacted."

Incidentally, although this discussion will understandably be classified under the category of euthanasia, please note that the term *euthanasia* hardly ever appears in the text, and for a very good reason. I am so convinced that euthanasia is a damaged and unsalvageable word as a reference to treatment termination that I have virtually ceased using it altogether, except for quotations and references, and I urge you to do the same. For euthanasia means too many different things to different people, ranging from Nazi atrocities to its original meaning of "good death." If used at all, it should refer to direct killing, not to treatment termination. "There is evidence that efforts to use the term *euthanasia* with any other sense than the one it has in current usage, i.e., direct killing, do not fully succeed." According to Paul Ramsey, the idea of direct mercy killing "is now unreformably part of the meaning the term will have in current usage."

Let us try, therefore, insofar as possible, when we are seeking to communicate with each other on treatment-termination decisions, to avoid the rhetoric, pro or con, of euthanasia. Let us simply avoid the term altogether, and substitute for it more descriptive phrases for our meanings. This would also imply that we cease trying to break down this many-faced term into different types, such as *direct voluntary, indirect voluntary, direct involuntary,* and *indirect involuntary euthanasia.* For the term itself has been too badly damaged to ever be recoverable as a useful term for discussion of treatment termination.

Another damaged term is *extraordinary means*. Although I value the intent of the tradition which speaks of *ordinary* and *extraordinary treatment*, I find these terms confusing rather than clarifying, especially on ever-closer inspection. What is extraordinary in one period of history (such as an amputation in the nineteenth century) becomes ordinary in another period. Paul Ramsey has persuasively shown that *ordinary* means mandatory or imperative while *extraordinary* simply means elective or nonobligatory forms of treatment. The courts have found this language opaque and obfuscating. I have abandoned the terms altogether, and found the communication process improved when I do.

The Vulnerability of Patient Confidence. The trust relation between physician, patient, and family, reinforced by legal constraints, has been at least two thousand years developing. Treatment cannot function without trust in the physician's integrity and his determination to prolong life. It is the only basis upon which a patient can radically put his future in the hands of another.

Guideline ten: *The patient's assumption that the doctor will struggle incessantly for his life is of great importance to the morale of the patient who may be summoning all his strength to fight illness.* Most doctors are relentlessly opposed to a broad relaxation of treatment-termination guidelines for this reason. The role of the physician is to heal. This role is diametrically opposed to the role of ending life. I personally do not feel that it is necessarily a social disaster when doctors view death as a failure, as some commentators do. For if that commitment is ever diluted, it may subtly undermine the patient's confidence and increase suspicion. The Hippocratic oath binds the physician's conscience: "To please no one will I prescribe a deadly drug nor give advice which may cause his death." "I swear . . . I will carry out a regimen for the benefit of the sick and will keep them from harm and wrong. To none will I give a deadly drug even if solicited."

The Fiduciary Relation. What is the extent of your physician's legal responsibility to you as patient and family? Prior to the time a doctor-patient relationship has been contracted, the physician does not owe any special duty to provide treatment to anyone. If an accident occurs, the law does not compel the doctor to stop and render aid, just as you and I are not legally required to try to rescue some one who is drowning.

The obligation is quite different however, where a doctor-patient relationship has been established, where services have been rendered and fees paid. For then the law presumes a steady reliance on the part of the patient that the physician will continue to treat him according to his best understanding and skill. This is called a *fiduciary relationship*. Once begun, the physician is legally obligated competently to carry out a particular treatment to an acceptable conclusion based on standard medical practice. Note this irony: the patient has a right to *assume* that his physician will treat him completely and competently. The physician, however, does not have the right to assume that the patient will give his or her consent to any and all treatment, but rather the physician must, in surgery for example, secure the consent of the patient before proceeding. Surgery without consent has technically been considered an assault and battery. Consent to surgery also assumes full disclosure of all relevant risk factors. This consent may on certain occasions be implied, as in emergencies where the patient is unconscious.

Anglo-American law on homicide defines as illegal any deliberate action which causes the death of another to occur, even if that action has some alleged or actual merciful intent. The desire to relieve pain does not change homicidal intent, according to legal tradition. That interpretation, which has been tested in many courts over many centuries, is the heir of a rich moral and medical tradition from Pythagoras, Augustine, Maimonides, and Paracelsus to the present which has given Western history a high view of the value of life, and a strong ethic that the physician must invariably be on the side of sustaining life and promoting health.

Apart from a court-sanctioned procedure for termination, any deliberate action you might ask your physician to take which is intended to bring about the death of a patient, even though done at the request of the patient and with merciful intent, might if carried out expose the physician to possible malpractice challenges or even criminal liability. For in the fiduciary relation, your doctor owes an affirmative duty of due care and professional treatment to his patient. This includes, for example, the duty to act to prevent suicide. If he should fail to exercise "reasonable care to prevent a suicide," he might well be subject to a civil suit involving liability for wrongful death. Some legal opinion, however, holds that "the physician's obligation to act affirmatively to prevent the patient's suicidal actions becomes less in direct proportion to the 'hopelessness' of the patient's condition and the extraordinary nature of the measures being utilized to maintain him" (Meyer). Apart from the *Quinlan* case, there is little legal precedent as yet to bolster this opinion, but it is likely that the courts in the future will move cautiously in this direction.

Specifically, the language of the law is this: "No criminal sanctions attach to omissions which cause harm to others, *unless* there is a legal duty to act." However, "Where there is a duty to act, deliberate nonfeasance with intent to cause death is, as a rule, punishable homicide." Thus guideline eleven: *Since the physician has a fiduciary duty to act to preserve the patient's life, you put your physician in a special difficulty if you ask him or her to assist in ending life, apart from a court-sanctioned procedure to terminate life support.*

Your relation with your doctor is legally considered a contractual relation, and thus based on mutual consent and binding obligation. The physician is obliged to continue treating "as long as the case requires." The patient, in this contract, has a right to assume that the physician will not withdraw from him a treatment so as to cause him any harm, much less death. The withdrawal of life-support systems is generally considered to operate under this rule. Under most circumstances, if the physician withdraws from you a means of life support that will cause death, he is potentially subject to the charge of abandoning care. This is true of any treatment causing harm, but all the more true of life-supporting treatment. For there the patient is by definition helpless, and often totally unable to express his preference or consent. This is why the courts have followed the maxim that once a life-support system has been initiated, the moral and legal predisposition is, on the whole, in favor of its continuance. The reasoning behind this maxim is difficult for many people to affirm, unless they have taken into consideration the basic nature of the fiduciary relationship.

The Rigor of the Law Moderated by Its Application. The traditional rigor of Anglo-American medical law is stated by jurist Norman St. John-Stevas: "Doctors or others who assist such persons to take their lives are held responsible as aiders and abetters or principals in the second degree, to the self-murder of another. They are principals in the first degree to murder if they administer the fatal dose themselves, whether or not the patient has given his consent." If the doctor's actions have the effect of "irritating or provoking the disease to operate more violently and speedily," he is technically liable to prosecution.

The rigor of criminal law, however, is tempered by its administration. In practice there have been few indictments, even fewer convictions, and juries are prone to acquit. It is extremely difficult for prosecutors to show cause of death or to prove intent, especially if there is no written evidence.

In the most famous American case, it was charged that a New Hampshire physician, Dr. Sanger "willfully and of his own malice aforethought did inject . . . air into the veins of Abbie Borroto, and with said air injection, feloniously, willfully, and of his said malice aforethought killed and murdered" his patient. He was acquitted, although his license to practice was temporarily suspended.

Guideline twelve: *Your physician is understandably more con-*

cerned to defend himself against civil actions for malpractice than against criminal liability. For criminal convictions against physicians are extremely rare, but many have been acrimoniously sued for malpractice and huge recoveries granted by juries that are sometimes resentful of the physician's power and wealth.

So the physician faces risks that you and I do not face, precisely because of his special legal duty to preserve life and health. The doctor may risk suspension of license, expensive litigation or official censure if he talks unilaterally about terminating life support apart from a court-sanctioned procedure.

There is one traditionally recognized exception to the rule that the physician's fiduciary responsibility prevents the shortening of life. That occurs when the physician administers a pain-killing medication which knowingly would tend to accelerate the death of a terminally ill patient. This is justified under the traditional rule of "double effect," for there are two effects of the drug: (1) the control of pain is its primary purpose, and (2) the fact that it tends to accelerate death is not its purpose, but only an incidental effect. The positive value of reducing pain must be judged greater proportionally than the risk taken in shortening life. If these conditions are present, neither the courts nor most moralists have found objection to the medical practice of administering pain-reducing drugs that tend to shorten life.

A somewhat similar dilemma appears in risky surgery, where the possible hope of recovery must be weighed against the risk of shortening life. Disconnecting life support, however, does not easily fit under this rule, since there the deliberate intent is to end life, not to make a proportional judgment on the risks taken in shortening life.

Family Consent. If the family has expressed its willingness to follow the physician's advice on treatment-termination decisions, then once having stated that, it will be the working assumption of the relationship unless someone calls it into question. So if you do not intend to imply such an authorization, do not make it.

Rather make it explicit to your physician that you expect to be included whenever crucial decisions are to be made.

The physician may prefer not to formalize consent from the family, but rather may act on the basis of implied consent. In doing so you should realize that he increases his risk and responsibility. He may be doing this in order to save the family from a painful moral struggle or possible disagreement. However, if you feel strongly that you as a family would prefer to be included directly in the decision-making process when the time comes, you should make that known to your physician in advance. He must, by law, take next-of-kin consent into account if the patient is unconscious or moribund. A trustful confidential relationship with the physician is likely to work in favor of the family's preferences being heard and respected.

The physician who has agreed to treat an unconscious patient without family consent may place himself in a difficult position of legal liability. If you are a friend of such a patient, the physician may wish to have your opinion, but cannot regard it as having the same weight under law as would the opinion of the next of kin or legal guardian.

It is naive, however, to assume that the family is invariably protective of the patient's interest. While most families doubtless have the best interests of the patient at heart, there are some for whom loss of time, money, and the emotional strain of long-term care may unwisely or unfairly influence a termination decision.

Patients and patient advocates, however, are increasingly unwilling merely to accept a physician's unilateral directive on these matters. Patients and families are now in the process of educating themselves about their legal and moral rights to be involved in end-care treatment decisions.

"Our ideal treatment team," according to Dr. Elisabeth Kübler-Ross, "includes the physician who treats the patient, any specialist who has been in on the case, a member of the clergy, the nurses, the social worker, and a consulting psychiatrist. This team should understand the needs not only of the dying patient, but also of his family. In the case of children we ask each other if we would continue treatment if this were our child? If the unanimous opinion is against any use of extraordinary means, we then present this decision to the family. We do not ask them for an opinion, but simply state our decision, adding that it would require a strong veto on their part to make us decide otherwise." Dr. Kübler-Ross's desire to help the family avoid guilt leads her into this slight overstatement. It is better, on the whole, if this decision is not "presented to" the family, but offered as a possibility to the family with a serious request for responsive dialogue and mutual decision.

An older elitist view argues that the physician unilaterally makes the decision, and then merely consults with the family whose consent is only advisory but not obligatory. According to this view, opinions expressed by the family—whether for continuation or discontinuation of active treatment—are nonbinding.

The obvious difficulty with this assumption is that there are many nontechnical and nonmedical factors which enter into a terminal-care decision. The physician is less well equipped to assess some factors than is the family. Anyway, the physician does not possess clear legal dominion over the incompetent patient. "Once the patient loses capacity to determine his own fate," advises bioethical legal counselor Meyer, "responsibility for decision making probably shifts to the next of kin (i.e., the family) as natural guardian. Determination of the patient's future would, then, rest with the family in consultation with the physician; the practitioner would not ordinarily have authority to make unilateral decisions."

Family responses to the physician may range from complete and unshakeable trust to persistent suspicion and proneness to malpractice threats. Every physician must make an intuitive judgment about where a given family lies on such a scale as he faces a decision to withhold or extend life support. The irony is this: malpractice threats may have the counterproductive effect of reinforcing the physician's instincts for a legally safer course of treatment continuation.

Suppose most family members consent to terminating life support but a minority have serious reservations. You should be ready for a cautious response from the physician. For if the consent of the family is not unanimous, it may increase his risk if a discontinuance decision is made.

Suppose your family is willing to continue long-term care for the hopelessly ill patient, but the physician knows that it would work a very serious hardship on you, including possible impoverishment of family resources. This might elicit a particular response from the physician that you should try to understand— the tendency to overstate the case for discontinuation so as to relieve the family of any potential burden of guilt. In a sincere attempt to alleviate unnecessary family anguish, the doctor may present his own ethical dilemma as if it were already decided, self-evident, not really a moral choice, but already determined on technical grounds. The family in such a case may be deprived of both moral responsibility and moral guilt. Guideline thirteen: *To the degree that the family or patient advocates propose to take upon themselves the responsibility for moral choice, their potentiality for bearing guilt also increases.*

Guilt potential is great because the decision is irretrievable. In most other moral choices one has the possibility of changing one's mind later. Not so about a choice to end life, either of one's own or another's. If a family urges a patient into surgery and the patient does not survive, they may experience guilt. If the family urges continued active treatment and the illness hopelessly worsens, they may experience guilt. But if they discontinue life support under ambiguous circumstances, the potential for guilt is maximal.

Christian worship celebrates God's forgiveness for our mistaken judgments and self-deceptions. The Sacrament of the Supper comforts those who experience guilt and penitently long for reconciliation with God and conscience. But the Christian eucharist at its best does not offer a cheap grace which blithely says, "No matter what you do, and no matter how callous you are, you are OK and can have an easy conscience." Too much pastoral advice has proceeded on this weak theological assumption that the average person sees through in a minute and that ordinary moral sensitivity finds abhorrent.

To those who follow the pleasure principle as a moral absolute, guilt will be experienced merely as a distracting invasion of some alien form of consciousness. The Jewish and Christian ethic, however, knows that guilt and injured conscience may function constructively toward correction, redemption, and greater wholeness.

Civil Action and Civil Disobedience. If the patient is an incompetent adult and legal guardianship has not yet been established, then guardianship is best sought apart from the question of treatment refusal or extension. If guardianship is granted, then treatment refusal may later be pursued in carefully paced stages. If, however, guardianship is not obtainable, and if, in extreme cases, the family is still of unanimously clear and good conscience that continued active treatment should not prolong suffering, they may find themselves considering two further alternatives: either to seek relief in the courts, or to engage in a conscientious act of civil disobedience with the willingness to stand trial if necessary under law for one's action.

Which of these two regrettable options would be, on the whole, better? Each has its disadvantages. Neither should be taken until all other options are exhausted. The special disadvantage of court action is that hard cases may tend toward precedent-setting implications that do not apply so well to more typical situations, so the law becomes skewed in peculiar directions. The special disadvantage of civil disobedience is that it tends overly to privatize legal responsibility and may inadvertently undermine respect for law in a society where respect for law is already deeply under fire.

28 Should Treatment Be Terminated?

What do we learn when a family places a treatment question before the courts asking an anticipatory sanction of a deliberate action leading to a person's death? The case is then removed from confidentiality into public knowledge and public sentiment, where first the courts and then the press are tempted to practice medicine. Under the blinding glare of public awareness, the court cannot easily afford to send a signal to society that there is any slackness in the state's determination to protect innocent life equally and unselectively.

Guideline fourteen: *Families of terminally ill persons should be aware of the special moral obligation on the courts to protect human life. If they ask for legal recourse under situations of extreme duress to allow death, they should expect the court to be rigorous at the point of defense of extant life on a nonselective basis.*

Is there any viable possibility of an act of civil disobedience under such conditions, where the family, after trying repeatedly and unsuccessfully to withhold consent to medical treatment, is clearly addressed by moral conscience with the unambiguous demand to terminate treatment on behalf of the suffering loved one? Although I would not presume to act as anyone else's conscience, I can affirm a long-standing ethical tradition which says that if the well-instructed conscience is clear and certain, there may be special instances in which it is necessary soberly to break an existing unjust law in order to achieve an otherwise impossible good, in which case one must be willing to stand responsibly under the law's judgment for such an action.

If medical or pastoral care is involved in the consideration of an act of civil disobedience, it has the duty to make clear several things: it must make clear that the individual understands that his action may be against current law, and that merciful motivation does not necessarily mitigate homicidal intent in the eyes of the law. Pastoral care must discern whether the conscience is entirely clear, since such a drastic and irremediable action as the ending of a life, even with the most compassionate intent, must not proceed on the basis of a divided or ambiguous conscience. Pastoral care must attempt to help the individual understand the consequences of his action. It will never lose sight of the sanctity of life, even under conditions of grave limitation and grotesque distortion. It will try to insure that all reasonable alternatives short of civil disobedience have been attempted prior to such an action, and there must be no disingenuousness on this point. No act of private conscience against law should ever occur thoughtlessly, imprudently, hastily, and without prayer and spiritual preparation for the consequences that are likely to follow.

Is There an Absolute Right to Bodily Self-Determination? We have left to the end of this chapter one of the most basic philosophical aspects of the question, "Who decides?" The intention of the law to provide equal protection to extant life raises knotty questions in our minds about what our individual rights are. Cannot I personally decide to end my own life? If not, why not?

There is a strong assumption in the modern mind that self-determination is an absolute moral value. The rhetoric of personal freedom reinforces this assumption. It seems so self-evident to unreflective modern individualism that we have an absolute right over our bodily life, even if in some extreme situations that means asserting the right to death, or to help relieve the suffering of a companion by assisting the dying process if necessary.

Few disagree, however, that the state has a clear duty to the potential suicide victim to intervene to prevent attempted self-destruction. This leads to one of our most crucial guidelines on individual consent: *Rightly or wrongly the legal assumption is that at the moment a person atempts suicide, he is in some sense temporarily not exercising a valid judgment in his best interests and therefore a bystander or police officer owes it to that person to restrain that temporary unwise judgment.* This reasoning is to some degree applicable to treatment termination decisions.

The precedent-setting Heston ruling forcefully argued that the state's interest in sustaining life in emergency medicine "is hardly distinguishable from its interest in the case of suicide. . . . It is commonplace for the police and other citizens, often at great risk to themselves, to use force or strategem to defeat efforts at suicide, and it hardly could be said that thus to save someone from himself violates a constitutional right."

This leads us unavoidably into a further exploration of the possibility of a legitimate right to suicide. It is sometimes imagined that a legitimate right to suicide was generally accepted and approved in the ancient world, but this is a misreading of the facts. Thebes and Athens denied funeral rites to suicides. Plato, Aristotle, Virgil, Caesar, and Ovid, and even Cicero all condemned suicide. Only a few of the Roman Stoics eulogized suicide as noble death. "One need not be wretched but by choice," wrote Seneca. "Do you like to be wretched? Life. Do you like it not? It is in your power to return from whence you came. . . . Just as I shall select my ship, when I am about to go on a voyage, or my house when I propose to take a residence, so shall I choose my death when I am about to depart from life." The act of taking one's own life, however, has been considered by Jewish and Christian moralists as one of the most radical and irreversible acts of nonresponsiveness to the grace of God, rejection of God's providence, and inordinate desire to control the conditions of life.

The Christian ethic of love calls us to be deeply empathic toward the desperate anguish that persons must feel when they are struggling with suicide. Historic Jewish and Christian injunctions against suicide must not diminish our compassionate responses toward attempted suicides and their families, nor blunt the efforts of religious communities to offer a context of care and hope.

That compassion, however, does not erase or negate the continuing strong Jewish and Christian moral injunctions against aggressions against one's own body or the ending of one's own life. In fact we have a well-developed tradition of reasoning about the taking of one's own life that is to some degree applicable to situations of the premature wishing for death amid serious illness.

That tradition of reasoning, for example, views martyrdom under a wholly different category than suicide, since in martyrdom (as in the case of Jesus or the Jews at Masada or the Christian martyrs of the Diocletian persecution) there is no thought of avoiding suffering or bemoaning the conditions of human existence, but rather a willingness to receive death under those specific conditions of historical alienation where the fury of evil makes a faithful life impossible. Thus martyrdom is essentially a grateful witness to the ground and giver of life rather than a protest against the wretched conditions of life.

The classical Christian perspective on suicide was stated by Augustine. His arguments penetrate into many of our deepest dilemmas on treatment termination. Augustine stated three reasons why no Christian believer can take his own life: First, because such an action leaves no possibility of repentance or restitution. It therefore stands as a uniquely problematic act of will that ends all possible future acts of will. It admits of no further corrective actions. Secondly, Augustine argued that such an action would be essentially a cowardly and freedom-disavowing response to the difficulties of life since it refuses to take on the conditions of human existence. The third reason is simply that it is specifically contrary to the command of God addressed in Scripture. For, "Thou shalt not kill," is addressed to oneself just as much as to any one else.

It was out of this Augustinian base that Thomas Aquinas developed several additional powerful arguments that have become traditional Christian doctrine. First, says Thomas, the taking of of one's own life is contrary to the call to be charitable, since charity also includes loving oneself. Secondly, it is contrary to the inclination implanted in every creature by the Creator which inclines one to protect oneself. The natural instinct of self-preservation calls us to resist risks of death insofar as we can. Third, Thomas developed a "social argument": each one of us is a part of a family and a community which has no way of benefiting from our presence or uniqueness after our death, and so if we take our lives away from ourselves we at the same time take our lives away from those others who might benefit from our existence, and we do so irremediably, and for all actual and possible communities to which we may belong. Thus, "to bring death upon oneself in order to escape the other afflictions of this life," concludes Thomas, "is to adopt a greater evil in order to avoid a lesser."

Some may think it inappropriate to inject into a discussion of treatment termination the classical arguments against taking one's own life. Upon reflection, however, the basic form of moral reflection for both seems to be quite similar. For are not the conditions that may drive persons to consider taking their own life often similar to those that might lead us to consider treatment termination—crushing and unmitigated suffering with no apparent hope of recovery?

How Then Does Treatment Termination Differ From Homicide and Suicide? I can imagine a troublesome impression forming in the mind of the reader at this point. For in this midst of your struggle with the question of whether to extend or terminate treatment of a loved one, suddenly you experience the law warning you that you must be careful that your action is not homicide, and the moralist warning you that you must be careful that your actions not be understood as an approval of suicide. Thus it seems useful at this point to draw some clear lines between four distinguishable terms: homicide, suicide, discontinuation of artificial life support, and *judicious neglect*. All involve the ending of life. All are actions which result intentionally in death. But they differ in intent and in the assessment of the victim's best interest.

These distinctions show that there are significant differences, despite similarities, between legitimate treatment termination and suicide. For in treatment termination one ends life only when there remains no reasonable hope of recovery from an illness that involves hopeless impairment, while in suicide one is willfully and intentionally seeking to end one's own life while there yet re-

HOMICIDE	SUICIDE	TREATMENT TERMINATION BY DISCONNECTING LIFE SUPPORT	TREATMENT TERMINATION BY "JUDICIOUS NEGLECT"
Directly causes death of another	Directly causes one's own death	Debatable whether it directly causes death of patient or not	Indirectly allows death of patient by not acting
Commits an action	Commits an action	Commits an action that allegedly allows the body to "return to its natural state"	Omits action amid a fiduciary relationship that ordinarily assumes the duty to act
In murder, occurs by premeditated malicious motive; in manslaughter by sudden passion due to provocation	Motivated by desire to escape the current conditions of one's own existence	Motivated by the desire to end hopeless suffering as quickly as possible	Motivated by the desire to end hopeless suffering when the next critical emergency arises

Rejects the victim's right to future life	Rejects one's own life even when suffering is not irreversible	Allows death by withdrawal of life support only under the extreme conditions of hopeless suffering	Allows death by natural cause only under the extreme conditions of hopeless suffering
Illegal	Decriminalized, but not condoned by law	Requires court-sanctioned procedure	Alleged to be a frequent supplement to standard medical practice

main significant possibilities of recoverable meaningful existence. According to this reasoning, we formulate our sixteenth guideline: *The closer a treatment termination decision comes to considering the ending of life while there yet remains any significant possibility of meaningful existence, the more does classical moral reasoning concerning suicide apply to such a decision.*

If it is beginning to seem to the reader that legal and moral reasoning makes it very difficult to terminate treatment, then a part but not all of our objective has been accomplished. For in a society where it is easy to end life, many lives will be ended too easily.

But it is far from our intention to argue that *under no circumstances whatever* may treatment be terminated. We are also searching for reasonable criteria by which responsible judgments may be made to terminate active therapeutic treatment in certain irreversible cases. So our next task is to spell out these criteria.

Who Decides?   35

2. BY WHAT GUIDELINES?

Should treatment ever be terminated? If we answer, "No, not ever," then we have no further moral struggle on treatment termination itself, but instead we have a new set of consequent moral problems, for example, how to finance medical care with increasing numbers of hospitalized patients on artificial maintenance systems.

But if we answer cautiously, "Seldom, but yes under some circumstances," then we have to search for clarity about what particular circumstances might justify termination. By what guidelines are we to make reliable judgments? What variables are likely to affect our decision in what order and with what weight?

There is, of course, no legal or moral impediment in turning off respiration or any other life-support apparatus when brain death has occurred. According to the Harvard criteria, "Death is to be declared, and *then* the respirator turned off." That is standard medical practice.

If, however, the patient has ony one of several forms of responsiveness, the criteria for brain death have not been met. Brain death is declarable only if there is no reflex responsiveness, a flat (unresponsive) electroencephalograph (EEG) reading of brain waves, a total absence of spontaneous breathing and movement, and total unawareness of external stimuli or inner needs. If any of these forms of responsiveness still exist, and therefore if brain death is not declarable, then we must proceed cautiously toward the following criteria. The discussion that follows applies to situations where treatment termination is arguable, but death is not at present declarable.

No Absolute Indicator. It would simplify things considerably if we could confidently isolate one single factor that invariably indicates treatment termination. We have many such factors that invariably indicate active treatment continuation—a strong will to live, a long-life prognosis or possible reversibility of the illness —no physician under standard medical procedures would terminate treatment if any one of these conditions were clearly present.

But is there any single indicator that absolutely and without exception points toward ending life-sustaining treatment? No. The two-column comparison in the Preface has already presented plausible objections to many of these alleged absolute indicators. Family preference, for example, cannot be an absolute indicator because it cannot override legal protections, standard medical practice, or patient preference to continue treatment. Neither is imminence of death an absolute indicator, since most patients prefer active therapeutic treatment until their demise. Even patient preference cannot be an absolute indicator, since the patient temporarily may be severely depressed, a fact that skews the consent process.

The one factor that comes closest to being a clear indicator of termination is the permanent loss of all higher mental function, the irreversible loss of all capacity to understand or experience reality consciously. Even in that case, however, the hopelessly comatose patient may not be invariably or immediately terminated, as we have seen in the *Quinlan* case, since (1) lack of unanimous consent from the family or guardian, physicians, hospital, or courts, may prevent or delay termination of treatment even if the majority of consenting persons think it wise; (2) a long life expectancy may make termination more rather than less problematic; and (3) it can be argued that exceptional cures are always possible. Thus our next major guideline is that *there is no single factor that points absolutely and invariably toward termination, so that if you knew the severity of that factor you would clearly know whether to terminate.*

If this is correct, then we must seek to understand how several factors may conspire so as arguably to indicate termination. This problem has received attention from our interdisciplinary team of physicians and scholars at Drew University. The Drew ad hoc Committee on Treatment Termination has, after detailed study, developed the following basic guideline for families, physicians, hospital ethics committees, and other consenting parties.

> *The Drew Criterion: If there is permanent loss of all cognitive function, corroborated by medical consultation, that is, permanently impaired understanding so as to offer no reasonable hope of recovery; and if there is irrefutable evidence that biological death is imminent, or where the dying process is assessed by medical practitioners as being in its last stages; and if the family members unanimously concur with the attending physician that active treatment of emergent complications should not be pursued; and if the patient's preference in such a circumstance is known by written document or reasonably implied; then the family may justifiably consent to withholding active treatment on new complications or emergencies, while continuing life support already instituted, so as to allow the terminal illness to take its course.*

This admittedly is a cautious guideline, not easily distortable, and yet it does allow that treatment may be licitly terminated under highly constricted conditions. While it does not answer all potential situations of arguable treatment termination, it does suggest a limited and safeguarded means by which termination decisions may proceed. The Drew criterion, of course, is merely a moral advisory for consenting parties, and not a law.

The Drew interdisciplinary committee limited itself to a single question: Under what conditions may consenting parties appropriately withhold active treatment upon which the life of a patient depends prior to irreversible cessation of brain function?

The committee, composed of a neurosurgeon, a cardiologist, a chemotherapist, a genetic ethicist, several bioethicists, a political theorist, a psychologist, a sociologist, a theologian, a hospital chaplain, a geriatric nurse, and an attorney, was modeled generally after the Harvard ad hoc committee on the definition of brain death. We attempted first to identify all variables relevant to treatment-termination decisions. As convener, I attempted a game-theory approach to these variables, seeking to design a forced choice simulation in which different combinations of these variables were present. Having collected and computed considerable data from the simulation, the committee finally attempted to formulate the most heavily weighted factors in the form of a moral advisory.

The game-theory approach was developed in the form of a card sort which was viewed as "an experiment in moral judgment." Each experimenter was given a set of 122 cards that were placed in twelve shuffled piles, under these categories:

AGE	MARITAL AND FAMILY STATUS	PATIENT PREFERENCE
SEX	SEVERITY OF IMPAIRED UNDERSTANDING	FAMILY PREFERENCE
RACE	PHYSICAL IMPAIRMENT	DISCOMFORT SCALE
SOCIO ECONOMIC-STATUS	LIFE EXPECTANCY	RELIGIOUS BELIEFS

A case was defined as a group of twelve cards made up of one card drawn from each shuffled pile.

Each experimenter drew and studied carefully a randomly selected "case" of twelve cards. He then was asked to make a conscientious decision as to whether treatment should be continued or discontinued at one of five levels:

HEROIC TREATMENT—Continue every viable treatment relevant and possible to this case, including seemingly "heroic" life-sustaining support systems indefinitely if necessary, with full determination to keep the patient alive at whatever cost.

ACTIVE TREATMENT—Continue, according to standard medical practice, to combat emergencies and diseases, continuing life-support systems already initiated, with the intent of sustaining life as long as is reasonably possible.

BENEVOLENT CRISIS ACQUIESCENCE—Continue palliative or comforting treatment, but do not actively treat new emergencies or complications, so as to allow death to take its course when the next major crisis arises. Life-support systems already begun would be continued, but new crises would be met with "judicious neglect."

DISCONTINUANCE—Continue feeding and palliative treatment, but withdraw a life-support system and thus allow the irreversible illness to take its course.

ABSOLUTE DISCONTINUANCE—Make the patient as comfortable as possible, but immediately withdraw all artificial life-support systems (including oral, throat or intravenous feeding, oxygen, blood plasma, antibiotics, and all except pain medication) so as to allow hopeless suffering to end as soon as possible.

Each participant recorded his level-of-treatment decision on a data report sheet, and then rank ordered the twelve cards in the order of their importance in the making of the decision. These rank orderings were then computer correlated for their mean variances and predictive values.

The limited availability of life-sustaining equipment could be figured into the simulation by drawing two cases and allowing them to compete for one support system. Participants were allowed to work on cases independently or in pairs or groups, provided they reported their decision had been arrived at together.

Three hundred and eighty-two randomly selected cases were judged and analyzed by this means. The data received was fed into a computer for a multiple regression analysis that enabled the committee to examine two resulting scales: (1) the perceived importance of the variables to the average participant, that is, which factor was felt to be most important by the greatest number of participants in most cases, and (2) the predictive value of each variable, that is, which of the twelve sets of variables has the greatest value in predicting outcomes.

Impairment of Higher Brain Function. The most important single finding of the Drew study has been the exceptionally heavy weight given to the severity of impaired understanding. The cognitive impairment factor alone accounted for 55.7% of the known predictors of outcome. If you know that factor alone, it will tell you more than half of what can be learned from an examination of all twelve factors together. The severity scale of the cognitive impairment cards ranged from "No cognitive impairment" to "No reasonable hope for any cognitive capacity in the future." These cards affected decisions far more significantly than any other set.

Five other variables were found to be considerably less important, yet they appeared recurrently enough that they are to be regarded also as significant factors:

Life expectancy (accounted for 37 percent of the known predictors). Life-expectancy cards ranged in severity from "This illness does not affect life expectancy" to "Irrefutable biological evidence of imminent death."

Discomfort scale (accounted for 9 percent of known predictors). Discomfort scale cards range from "No pain or suffering" to "Unrelenting, terrible pain and suffering with no relief from medication."

Physical impairment (accounted for 9 percent of known predictors). Physical impairment cards ranged from "No physical impairment" to "Permanent loss of respiratory function requiring intensive care."

Patient preference (accounted for 8 percent of the known predictors). Patient preference cards ranged from "Strongly affirms continued full treatment" to "Signed document expressly indicating desire to refuse treatment; hoping for death soon."

Family preference (accounted for 1 percent of known predictors). Family preference cards ranged from "Family strongly prefers continuance" to "Family wants immediate termination."

Although discomfort and physical impairment claim our attention emotively, they turn out to be much less important as actual predictors of decision making than we at first expected. The Drew study statistically reinforced the hypothesis stated by Diana Crane (1975) that physical impairment is less important in treatment-termination decisions than many imagine. It becomes important only when linked with other primary indicators. Other variables such as sex, age, socioeconomic status, religious beliefs, and marital status were found to be insignificant in predictive value in determining outcomes.

What severity of cognitive impairment suggests treatment termination, assuming agreement of consenting parties? The guideline is: *The closer the patient is to the permanent loss of all higher brain function, the greater would be the society's probable consensus toward allowing benign neglect in the treating of new infections, and the less is the moral constraint upon the physicians and family to pursue active treatment.*

The importance the Drew data assigned to cognitive impairment is corroborated by the views of Dr. Elisabeth Kübler-Ross, who writes:

> We should not discontinue life-saving measures as long as the patient's brain is functioning. . . . As long as the patient can express his needs, I think we should maintain a support system,

because it means that the patient is still a functioning human being. If the patient is nonfunctioning and not communicating, the family, the physician, and the interdisciplinary team have to get together and make a joint decision. Each case should be discussed on an individual basis. I don't think we have valid generalized criteria, except for the definition of death, as outlined in Henry Beecher's *Harvard Report*.

Imminence of Death. Should imminence of death be a primary indicator to terminate active treatment? Here law and medicine have conflicting norms. The equal-protection clause, as we have explained, protects the life of the person very near death just as vigilantly as it does the person just born. If we view a court ruling to terminate life support under the broader analogy of a death sentence, as some do, then there is no reason to see life expectancy as an influencing factor. If anything, in a criminal death sentence, the probability of an imminent death or a short life expectancy is likely to soften the decision rather than harden or hasten it.

However, a different sort of reasoning has been developed by the American Medical Association in its 1973 ruling that "when there is irrefutable evidence that biological death is imminent," the decision may be made by the patient or family in consultation with the physician to withhold "extraordinary means" of treatment.

But what specifically is meant by "irrefutable biological evidence of imminent death"? That is a professional medical prognostic judgment that could vary some, but not much, from physician to physician, and if necessary could be supported with empirical evidence, such as EKG and EEG readings, blood pressure, blood count, temperature, and respiratory function. However, there is a danger that this imminent-death criterion might be uncritically expanded to include the middle to later stages of the dying process. I think it is best applied when the evidence for imminent cessation of vital functions is clear and distinct. "Imminent" means "threatening to occur immediately," not "fairly soon."

Terminal illness, incidentally, has no sharp definition. One symposium has defined it as "a diseased state whose presence raises in the mind of physicians, patient or family an expectation of death as a direct consequence of the illness." Thus the notion of terminal illness hinges strongly on prognosis, the inexact science of the prediction (prognostication) of the course of the disease.

There is, of course, a general sense in which everyone alive is moving toward death at varying paces. One might conceivably look upon any moment of life as a stage in the dying process, broadly construed. We are well advised, however, to define the dying process as a specific set of medical conditions where the signs of life are rapidly deteriorating and moving inexorably toward the cessation of all function. Glaser and Straus have identified seven stages of this "dying trajectory": the patient's condition is defined as hopeless; the family and hospital staff, and (if possible the patient) make initial preparations for the eventuality of death; at some point there is nothing more to do medically except provide palliative treatment; the final descent, which may take weeks or days or merely hours; the last hours; the death watch; and death itself.

Some rabbinic references define an imminent death as a condition where the individual is expected to die within three days or less. That traditional designation conceivably could be proposed as a modern criterion, buttressed by the probability estimates of medical technology.

I would prefer to state the "imminent death" guideline as follows: *The nearer the moribund patient is to immediate death, the greater would be the moral and social consensus toward allowing benevolent crisis acquiescence in the treating of new infections, if that is by unanimous consent in the best interests of the patient, and the less would be the moral constraint upon the physician and family to pursue active treatment.* This princi-

44   Should Treatment Be Terminated?

ple, of course, should not override patient preference or family preference.

These two guidelines hinge on a correspondence between what the Drew interdisciplinary committee took to be commonsense moral reasoning and a preliminary empirical assessment of social consensus. The proposed "social consensus" has, in our minds, the status of a hypothesis for further empirical validation. The consensus of our independent raters and experimenters does not, of course, mean that the entire society or other societies will necessarily share that consensus precisely. But our initial attempts to gather card sort data from socioeconomic and cultural groups different from our own (for example, from one group of low-income workers and from another group of oriental students) have reinforced our hypothesis that the consensus of our experimenters is not substantially different from a broader consensus based on more general forms of crosscultural awareness.

Some may wonder how we moved from social consensus to moral judgment without claiming too much for either. For it is possible to have a moral consensus that is morally wrong. In that case ethics cannot be simplistically derived from poll-taking. And yet the assessment of current and historical consensus remains the basis of viable legislation and court sanctions, in dialogue with legal precedents. So although we believe that individual conscience may be more refined and sensitive than the social consensus, that cannot imply that the social consensus can be ignored in any matter of public policy. And yet social consensus is extremely hard to assess accurately, as we have seen in our criticism of poll-taking, since the salient complexities tend to be reduced to meaningless generalities. It was in an effort to more accurately get at this social consensus as it pertains to these complexities that we devised our card-sort and game-theory approach to finding out how people rank order variables in theoretical cases of irreversible illness. We believe that we have identified (in a preliminary way that calls for further study) the basic shape of that social consensus. But we cannot and do not claim, in a simple sense, that if a majority of persons decide on termination in a particular case, it is in some final sense a correct moral judgment. We can only commend these data for your good individual judgment, as a guide, salve, or challenge to your conscience, however they may address you.

Summary of Influencing Factors. Now I am ready to summarize the twelve factors that should be weighed in a decision to extend or discontinue treatment in irreversible cases. There are three levels of influencing factors:

PRIMARY INDICATORS	SECONDARY INFLUENCES	SPECIAL CONSIDERATIONS
1. Permanently impaired understanding or communicative capacity	6. Discomfort, or degree of experienced suffering including mental anguish	9. Age and life expectancy
2. Documented or inferable patient consent	7. Unsalvageable physical impairment	10. Degree of bodily invasion of the life-support apparatus
3. Family consent, unless lacking unanimity	8. Limited availability of life-sustaining equipment or medical resources	11. Costs to the family and/or to society

4. Medical pro- fessionals' con- sent, unless lacking una- nimity	12. Religious be- liefs or moral convictions
5. Irrefutable bio- logical evi- dence of im- minent death	

Cautiously applying this trilevel interpretation of claims, we now come to the principal guideline that governs the weighing of these claims: *Benevolent crisis acquiescence becomes arguable only if all primary indicators are present, or if secondary and special considerations are sufficiently weighty to override the absence of one of the primary indicators.* If, for example, there is permanently impaired understanding and imminent death, but a serious lack of family consensus, the moral disposition would not favor treatment termination. If, however, there were irreducible suffering, a high degree of bodily invasion of life support and unconscionable costs to society, these considerations could override the absence of family consent.

Suppose a patient still has a six-month life expectancy and full cognitive awareness (lacking primary indicators) and yet there is unanimous consent from the patient, family and physician to terminate treatment of a cancer patient who is suffering and wishes to die. This guideline suggests that there would have to be substantial secondary and special considerations (such as unavailability of life-supporting equipment or extreme mental anguish or total physical incapacitation) in order for a hospital ethics committee to justify termination in the absence of the key primary indicators. Although this is our most crucial general guideline for weighing termination variables, it obviously requires good and wise judgment for its situational application, and one could conceive of many borderline cases that might present themselves as arguable exceptions.

The most thoroughgoing empirical study of physician's judgments in terminal illness was conducted by sociologist Diana Crane. Her conclusions correspond very closely to our distinction between primary and secondary influences:

> Two considerations are of great importance. First, is the patient salvageable? In other words, if he survives an acute crisis, can he be maintained at a reasonable level of functioning for a considerable period of time? Second, has the patient's condition affected his physical functioning only or his mental functioning as well? According to this survey, it appears that physicians would rank patients in the following order in terms of how actively they would treat them: (1) the salvageable patients with a physical deficit only; (2) the salvageable patient with severe mental deficit; (3) the unsalvageable patient with physical deficit only; and (4) the unsalvageable patient with mental deficit.

This rank ordering is consistent with the Drew data.

There are "three factors which play important roles in the physician's decision, according to Crane, "prognosis, type of deficit, and the consent of the patient or his agent." Agreeing that these are crucial factors, the Drew study modifies and elaborates Crane's conclusions in two ways: (1) by assuming that it is not just the physician who is making the moral choices, but all consenting parties; and (2) to Crane's three factors must be added the discomfort scale, the extent of bodily invasion and several other special considerations which although lower in importance than any of the above, become influential under particular circumstances.

Remember, no one factor is an absolute indicator of termination. Active treatment termination is legitimized only by a combination of factors, weighing primary indicators most heavily and special considerations least.

48   Should Treatment Be Terminated?

The Discomfort Scale. The assessment of the degree of discomfort is not a simple or easy judgment, since it includes subjective factors that are knowable only to the sufferer. If, however, you were to imagine a scale of 100 points in which 0 is no pain or suffering and 100 is the most unrelieved anguish of body and spirit, it would be possible for independent raters to place different descriptions of discomfort on such a scale and then to make a general ranking of types of discomfort. This is exactly what the Drew experiment did.

There apparently are several factors that enter into our judgment about how uncomfortable a particular condition is. If the length of time the discomfort has been experienced is already great, that, we found, decreases our assumed tolerance for future pain or suffering. If the length of future time the discomfort is likely to be endured is greater, the illness will be perceived as higher on the discomfort scale. If there is a possibility of eventual relief, the suffering will be assessed at a lower level. If the pain is such that it tends to rob the person of all meaningful present functioning, the discomfort is far greater, whereas even considerable pain seems easier to endure, even under conditions of irreversibility, if the person is able to carry on some (even minimal) other normal functions beside struggling against pain.

To the degree that the person experiences suffering in a warm, supportive, encouraging, and familiar environment, we found the discomfort expressed as proportionally lower. But to the degree that the convalescent environment is experienced as alienating, depersonalizing, cold, intractable, or hostile, the discomfort will be evaluated as demoralizing and relatively unmanageable. To the degree that the physical pain increases anxiety or is accompanied by emotional conflict, it will be perceived as higher on the discomfort scale, whereas even greater pain with less anxiety or inner conflict is likely to be considered more manageable. To the degree that the pain affects negatively not only the body but the spirit, the hidden springs of self-affirmation and the inner emotive life, it will be perceived as higher on the discomfort scale. Finally, and most basically, to the degree that the pain negatively affects the "will to live" or the capacity to affirm life, it will be regarded as much higher on the discomfort scale than similar pain surrounded by life affirmation.

These complexities necessitate the following rather detailed formulation of the discomfort guideline: *The moral disposition is strongly toward active treatment continuation if discomfort and relievable pain are not linked with imminent death or loss of cognitive function. Discomfort becomes an arguable influence in a termination decision to the degree that irreducible pain has already been experienced a long time and is expected to continue without relief so as to reduce severely all other meaningful functions, and to the degree that the context of discomfort is perceived as intractably alienating or is accompanied by anxiety and emotive conflict so as to affect the will to live and the very sources and ground of self-affirmation. Just to that degree the severity of discomfort understandably will enter into a level of treatment decision, never as absolute indicator, but as a reinforcement for other primary indicators and secondary and special considerations.*

Physical Impairment. While the discomfort scale measures the degree to which suffering is subjectively experienced as demoralizing to the will to live, the physical-impairment scale measures the degree to which physical function is objectively limited by an illness.

Imagine a scale on which 0 is no physical impairment and 100 is the most unsalvageable form of physical impairment. Independent raters could do card sorts of different types of incapacities ranking them in terms of perceived severity. This is exactly the approach we took in the Drew study.

We found that several criteria appeared to be implicitly operating in judgments about severity of physical impairment: A physical impairment is perceived as relatively severe to the extent that it (1) involves the permanent rather than temporary loss of function; (2) adversely affects the communication process; (3) requires intensive care or heroic medical facilities; (4) decreases mobility; (5) implies an unrelieved future of convalescence or dependence upon nursing services; and (6) is accompanied by mental anguish or sustained depression.

How heavily should a physical impairment be weighed when the patient has full consciousness and death is not imminent? When the Drew study began to sort out probable termination variables, we assumed that the severity of physical impairment would be regarded by many as a factor of the highest importance. We found, to our amazement, that it ranked far below cognitive impairment and life expectancy in its predictive value.

Guideline twenty-three is suggested for weighing the severity of physical disability: *The moral predisposition is strongly toward active treatment continuation for any but the most severe physical impairments in combination with other primary indicators (cognitive loss, imminent death, and concurrent consensus).*

Thus some of the classical arguments for terminating treatment on the basis of repugnance or gross disfigurement, crippling, or amputation, seem to be outmoded by the development of artificial limb technology, plastic surgery, and other rehabilitative therapies. The quadriplegic was regarded by raters as one of the most severe types of potential physical impairment. But, "If you visited some of these [quadriplegic] patients and saw what they are able to do, you would be surprised to see that they find meaning in their lives and are productive," writes Kübler-Ross. "As long as they have their brains, as long as they can still think, and use their eyes and their ears, and communicate, they should be given all the help possible to show them that life can still be meaningful and beautiful."

Paul Ramsey strongly argues that there is "no duty to use useless means." This judgment hinges on one's estimate of "whether there is a reasonable hope of success" in saving the person's life. Kieran Nolan has concluded that "the one general positive guideline" for treatment termination is that "the use of any means should be based on what is commonly termed a 'reasonable hope of success.'" "If so," says Ramsey, "the moral meaning of dispensable means would seem to reduce without remainder to a determination of an irreversible 'process of dying.'" With Ramsey, I doubt that this is an absolute indicator, although it should be weighed proportionally. For one could conceive of a long-term terminal illness in which irreversibility were clearly agreed upon by consulting physicians, and yet it would be evident to all that continued life support would be called for, as in the irreversible heart ailment of an eminent philosopher whose life expectancy was several years and whose cognitive capacities were completely unimpaired by the illness. Most would agree that such a person should receive oxygen, respiration, cardiac resuscitation, and whatever else was necessary, even though his condition were defined as irreversible with no hope of recovery.

An entire book could be filled with remission stories alone. I mention only one of them, out of a file of many dozens that have been sent to me. In 1962 a Soviet physicist, Lev Landau, was in a serious accident in Moscow. His situation was thought to be unsalvageable: skull fractured, brain lacerated, nine ribs, pelvis, and leg fractured, left arm paralyzed, severe abdomen contusions, ruptured urinary bladder. He was left deaf, blind, speechless, and without reflexes by the accident. He was in a coma for two months. He was treated by numerous physicians, who did not give up. Four days after the accident, Landau reportedly "died," according to certain criteria—his blood pressure and pulse disappeared; he had a flat EEG, and no reflex responses. The physicians, however, refused to turn off the respirator. They continued to transfuse blood, provide intravenous adrenalin and digitalis. Amazingly, life gradually returned. Although three times in the following week he almost died, five weeks later he recognized a close friend. Eleven months later he was able to sit up in bed and accept a Nobel Prize. Although he never fully recovered, he lived six more years in comparatively good health.

The Extent of "Bodily Invasion." In discussing the extent to which the right to privacy legitimately may affect a treatment-termination decision, the New Jersey Supreme Court devised a novel criterion in the *Quinlan* decision which, if upheld by subsequent court rulings, may provide some guidance in difficult cases: The state's interest in preservation of life "weakens and the individual's right to privacy grows as the degree of bodily invasion increases and the prognosis dims. Ultimately there comes a point at which the individual's rights overcome the state's interest."

There is some reason to doubt that the metaphor of "bodily invasion" is the most apt one to describe a life-saving device. For an invasion implies the attack of something that aims to do damage, while a life-support system aims only to preserve and protect life. However, if the issue is seen essentially from the point of view of the individual's right of privacy, as the higher court did in *Quinlan* case, then the principle may be to some extent helpful in cases where the support apparatus is viewed as serving no meaningful function whatever.

One of the ironies of the *Quinlan* decision was that the very basis upon which this faithful Catholic family and their priest won a favorable decision was the notorious *Griswold* (contraception) case, in which the Catholic *magisterium* was adamantly on the opposite side of the privacy issue. To compound the irony for American Catholics (as distinguished from Rome, which anxiously warned American Catholics of the hidden dangers of the "right to death" rhetoric), the *Quinlan* ruling specifically drew the analogy between the right to privacy in abortion and the right to privacy in treatment termination: "Presumably this right [of privacy] is broad enough to encompass a patient's decision to decline medical treatment under certain circumstances, in much the same way as it is broad enough to encompass a woman's decision to terminate pregnancy under certain conditions." It is this unwelcome analogy that is destined to trouble the Catholic conscience in the future.

Interpreted very cautiously, however, the "extent of bodily invasion" criterion can, I think, be viewed as a special consideration in a termination decision, as distinguished from a primary indicator, provided the metaphor is cautiously understood. The guideline may be restated for our purposes as follows: *To the degree that the artificial life support apparatus is by consensus perceived as an alien encroachment upon natural bodily processes serving no meaningful purpose, and to the degree that any hope of significant recovery dims, that is the extent to which the right to privacy impinges upon a decision to terminate. Conversely, the right to privacy is less and less applicable to the extent to which the treatment measures are supportive of natural bodily processes, and to the extent to which some hope of recovery or continued meaningful existence remains.*

Limited Availability of Life-Support Resources. Under emergency conditions where there are limited intensive-care facilities, who has the greater right to them? Does it not seem self-evident that the person who has the greatest chance for recovery should have the respirator? Many would argue this way. However, a more understandable, administrable, and fairer alternative is a purely equalitarian view of the value of human existence, as distinguished from a view that measures the value of a given life in relation to its assessed quality or probable chances for recovery. The resulting guideline: *Life-sustaining equipment should be offered to those who need it on a first-come, first-serve basis, on the assumption that every life is of equal value, even though the possibilities of recovery are varied.* If an elderly patient on a life-support system elects to give up his place in favor of some younger patient who has a better chance of recovery, that decision should be made by the patient himself, rather than by a review committee or team of "experts" whose lives are not at stake.

Medical resources have never in human history been available in superabundance. In military combat, to use a classical example, where many lie wounded, medical personnel must make forced choices about who to treat. Military medicine traditionally has sorted out three groups of patients under such circumstances: those who are most likely to recover if given immediate treatment, who are given preferential treatment; those who are likely to recover only if given long-term treatment, who are treated next; and those who are not likely to recover even if treated, who are temporarily set aside. This has sometimes been called *triage*, after the French term *trier* "to select or sort out" something into gradations of more and less hopeful possibilities.

There are several defects in applying triage to end-care decisions: it is an ethic devised under the conditions of emergency, which cannot be easily or simply translated into the conditions of relative normalcy. Triage is a military ethic, designed to facilitate military objectives. It tends to preserve the maximum fighting capability of an army, and therefore does not regard patients as standing on an equal basis. This means that it makes harsh judgments about the value of a given life exclusively in terms of its usefulness to the military effort. The socioeconomic classes that are least likely to get a fair shake by such utilitarian judgments are obviously the lower, poorer, and less influential classes and the oppressed.

Benevolent Crisis Acquiescence. Let us assume that we have unanimously decided in good conscience to terminate treatment of a patient on an artificial life-support system. Should the physician merely disconnect the machine, or should the termination proceed in accordance with some more organic medical philosophy? Here the quasi-traditional medical concept of "judicious neglect" has wisely argued against the abrupt termination of a life-support system as a legitimate form of standard medical practice. "Judicious neglect" is searching for a middle ground between an overt action immediately ending life and the continuation of active therapeutic treatment. "Judicious neglect" has traditionally meant that palliative treatment continues, and life support already instituted continues, but new emergencies are not to be vigorously battled nor are new infections or complications to be actively treated.

Can Judeo-Christian ethics subscribe to the theory of "judicious neglect"? Before giving a conditional affirmative answer, I must state two objections: (1) The term itself is poorly chosen. For how can treatment, which is the physician's duty, ever really amount to neglect? Passive acquiescence to the inexorable course of irreversible illness is hardly the same as neglect, which implies a failure to give due attention. It is for this reason that I have come to use the term *benevolent crisis acquiescence* as a more descriptive phrase for this view, instead of *judicious neglect*. For there may come a point at which it is consensually clear that to acquiesce to irreversible illness is (far from disregarding or neglecting the patient's needs) in the patient's best interests.

(2) Logically, the concept of withholding treatment as a form of treatment is a contradiction in terms. This is why the notion of "judicious neglect" has not entered fully into the mainstream of "standard medical practice." The conscience of the medical community is not yet clearly formed on how and when it is to be employed. It is one of the grey areas of medical ethics.

Despite these objections, the approach of *"benevolent crisis acquiescence" (or "judicious neglect") is more appropriate and ethically preferred as a mode of treatment termination than the abrupt and deliberate disconnection of equipment that currently is sustaining life* for the following reasons:

1. Benevolent crisis acquiescence continues to supply food, palliative medicine, and all possible forms of comfort to the moribund patient during his final struggle, rather than abruptly terminating life.
2. Benevolent crisis acquiescence does not in any way hasten death or attempt to prolong life by means of treatments other than those already instituted. By means of a benevolent pas-

sivity amid new crises or emergent complications, it simply acquiesces to incipient death, if this is in the best interest of the patient, without the withdrawal or withholding of treatment or life support previously provided.

3. If the patient truly is in an irreversible condition and if all reasonable hope of recovery is gone, and if death is a near-term probability, then the length of time of irreversible suffering is likely to be short in any event. This is a crucial point since the argument for direct disconnection usually centers on the advantage of shortening the length of time of irreversible suffering.

4. Whereas disconnection of life support arguably is a cause of death, benevolent crisis acquiescence does not *do* anything to hasten death or take any direct, active intervention which could arguably be viewed as the cause of death.

5. Although it may take longer for death to ensue (its alleged chief disadvantage), it is less subject to widespread abuse than is the more arbitrary act of "pulling the plug."

6. It proceeds under a more organic understanding of medical care than does the mechanical disconnection of electrical equipment as the final ignominious event in the person's life.

Cost Factor. Life-support medicine is very costly. Intensive care often runs $400 per day. The per-hour fee for the use of operating rooms is often over $100. Surgeon's fees for a single operation may cost many thousands of dollars. Even a live-in home health aide may require $40 per day.

I am not satisfied with the purist idealism that says cost factors have nothing whatever to do with treatment decisions. Neither was Pope Pius XII who in his 1957 declaration on "The Prolongation of Life" gave special attention to the importance of "grave burdens" of care on the family in considering treatment termination. But at what point may long-term medical costs legitimately be weighed as a secondary factor in considering the termination of treatment?

The guideline is this: *To the extent that the cost of life support is potentially impoverishing to the uninsured or inadequately insured patient and his family; and to the extent that inordinate cost increases the potential guilt being borne by the patient for placing heavy long-term burdens on loved ones; and to the extent that unusual expenditure of resources is truly futile with no reasonable hope of recovery, then the cost of continued treatment is likely to be considered as a supplementary factor to primary and secondary influences (often more poignantly by the patient himself than by his family) in a treatment-termination decision, and be weighed alongside other claims in the light of the available resources of the family and society.*

Three qualifications must be stated, however, if cost is to enter at all as a supplementary factor in the decision-making process: First, in advanced industrial societies, most persons are covered by some form of health insurance, and thus full direct cost is seldom borne exclusively by the family. Some costs are borne by the society as a whole, by taxpayers, or by those who pay insurance premiums. If the family or patient is poorly insured, however, cost may loom much more personally as a potentially weighty factor. Second, moral conscience rebels against making the value of life a budget item, to be weighed against whatever else money will buy. Third, there is an obvious disadvantage to patients and families in low socioeconomic classes in allowing cost even to figure at all into termination decisions. When cost becomes decisive, the poor will be the last to receive life support and the first to be terminated.

Quality of Life or Equality of Life. Should "quality of life" replace "sanctity of life" and "equal protection" as a legal and medical criterion for judging whether life should continue? Traditionally the judicial system has understood itself as unselectively responsible for the protection of human life. No duty is more elemental to the definition of the state than the protection of life. This political responsibility has been historically linked with the religious affirmation of the sanctity of life.

Should the courts enter into the hazardous and unprecedented arena of attempting to make value judgments about which persons' lives are relatively valuable or viable enough to continue living? If the courts enter this arena, where is the line to be drawn? Wouldn't we expect many overly burdened guardians of demented or incapacitated wards, of newborn defectives, and of senile persons to test the limits of such a precedent? How many innocent persons would become potential targets of court-sanctioned terminations under such circumstances? The state must protect the lives of these wards, incompetents, and sick people, not with ambiguous language about "quality of life" according to someone's definition, but equally and nonselectively.

There is a serious danger that "quality of life" can inadvertently become an upper-class elitist concept. "Equality of life" is more likely to be preferred by the poor as a principle for making treatment judgments.

Those who are concerned more with immediate sympathetic relief for anguished families than with the hazardous consequences for thousands of defenseless incompetents in the future, may find the equal-protection tradition hard to swallow. But its deeper instincts are sound and well tested historically. The alternatives to it are objectionable. For *if legal guardians are allowed independently to judge the worth and viability of human life, then we should not be surprised to see many terminations of newborn defectives, retardates, genetically handicapped, senile, and feebleminded persons whose lives could end under lax involuntary termination rulings.* Generally the courts have been wise to disallow broad constructions. (Even in the Quinlan ruling an elaborate procedure for hospital ethics committee review was proposed.) For what if families with less than worthy motives should wish desperately to be relieved of the frustrations, burdens, and financial responsibilities of caring for gravely sick loved ones

—would not the temptation be overwhelming to plead with the physician to end life prematurely, and even perhaps to seek out a hospital lenient on treatment termination?

We have seen similar abuses in the case of abortion. They would be all the more compounded in terminal cases where large sums of money awaited distribution among potential heirs. What is to prevent these potential abuses if not a rigorous law of nonselective protection of life? Although these are frightening thoughts, and should be, we must not be so optimistically predisposed as to expect that all physicians and families of sick persons would unerringly be free of unconscious motivations and aggressions which might lead to unjust actions.

Most "quality of life" language, upon close examination, is found to be vague, infinitely plastic and expandable. Courts and legislatures should give firm resistance to people who want to end life, for example, when it does not come up to their individual or esoteric standards of a "capacity to live a communicative life," or "when the patient stops being a historic man," or "human qualities," or "the capacity for love and tenderness." All such generalized and unsafeguarded language differs markedly from the cautious, self-limiting, and highly safeguarded criteria we have attempted to offer here.

Patient as Vegetable? One phrase that recurs incessantly in the medical descriptions of coma is "persistent vegetative state." Is this an accurate metaphor to describe comatose patients who have lost cognitive function but who continue to have many other forms of responsiveness? *Jewish and Christian moral thought should call upon neurologists to abandon the "patient as vegetable" analogy, and speak instead of a prolonged comatose condition or chronic state of low-level responsiveness.*

The analogy invites a particular set of moral responses, especially the treating of the living patient as if he or she were a vegetable. We do not even call deceased persons "vegetables" in our society, yet both popular language and neurological practice call living patients vegetables. This amounts to a linguistic predisposition and rationale to act as if the patient were a vegetable. It provides a convenient language for the thoughtless predisposition of crucial moral decisions. It is a pejorative, prejudicial, and dehumanizing use of metaphor.

Jewish and Christian religious consciousness has, to my knowledge, offered very little resistance to this metaphor. Yet its continued usage is inconsistent with the Jewish and Christian understanding of human selfhood, the providence of God, and the special value of human life as God's gift. It is time that religious communities begin asking physicians who use this term, "Just what do you mean by *vegetable?*"

The Wedge. The moment the courts and legislatures begin to make selective judgments about whose life deserves preservation, they enter a realm frighteningly similar to the kinds of judgments made in Nazi Germany about whose life was worth living, and whether the lives of psychological, physical, and racial "defectives" could be justly terminated by the state.

Involuntary mercy death was supported by many avant-garde intellectuals in the early twenties, but the appalling experience of Germany caused the idea to be generally discredited. On 1 September 1939, Adolf Hitler secretly signed an order calling for the "mercy killing" of persons who were mentally defective or incurably ill. The value of a person's life was harshly assessed purely in terms of its usefulness to the state. Victims included epileptics, psychotics, senile patients, and many others who were presumed to be "useless to society."

It is important to note that medical professionals, including psychiatrists, hospital administrators, and physicians, collaborated with these orders. There was apparently little resistance. An estimated 275,000 lives were ended in Germany euthanasia centers; many were foreign laborers alleged to be suffering for "incurable tuberculosis." Hitler's reasons were utilitarian: to provide more hospital beds for persons who were judged to have some "reasonable probability of recovery," and to "conserve the society's resources" (reasons still being offered today). At first top secret, it was halted in 1941 when rumors began circulating that wounded German soldiers and unproductive workers might be done away with. But the euthanasia program became a trial run for a holocaust machine, the gas chamber, which was later to be used to murder millions of Jews. This is why the mere mention of the term *euthanasia,* despite its original Greek meaning of "good death," evokes in the modern mind the specter of mass destruction.

The German philosophical idealists who first proposed involuntary euthanasia and the Nazi technicians who later carried it out give us our most horrifying historical example of the "wedge" theory of the relaxation of a strict view of the sanctity of human life. Guideline thirty summarizes this view: ***Once the sanctity of life precedent is broken, the abuses tend to expand, usually under the pretense of idealism.*** "Once a concession about the disposability of innocent life is made in one sphere, it will inevitably spread to others," comments Norman St. John-Stevas. "The recognition of voluntary euthanasia by the law would at once be followed by pressure to extend its scope to deformed persons and imbeciles, and eventually to the old and any who could be shown to be burdensome to society."

Dr. Heifetz at first sounds reasonable in stating: "I do not believe life is warranted if it cannot be lived with some measure of grace and dignity." But imagine that same statement being made by a Stalinist prison official or Nazi physician or South African racist. I shudder to think how such a rule might be applied by some with less worthy motives than Dr. Heifetz. It depends entirely on the good judgment of the person making such statements. That is just the point, and that is why loose "quality of life" criteria should never end up on the statutes.

Sanctity of life has never been regarded by Jews and Christians as a "secondary ethical concept," as Heifetz claims. "The sanctity of man," writes Heifetz, "implies the sanctity of a being with human qualities." But when we ask what are these "human qualities" the lack of which would warrant the ending of life, Heifetz answers, "tenderness, compassion, love, awareness, thoughts, memory." If, however, the sanctity of your life depends upon whether someone else judges that you are capable of love or memory, that is totally different from what has historically been meant by the sanctity of life. There are many persons who have a low capacity for love and tenderness, but for whom there is no warrant for ending their lives. Sanctity of life, in the Western moral tradition, does not depend on whether someone judges you capable of memory, compassion, or thinking, but essentially on the sheer fact that you are alive and the assumption that life is an incomparable gift.

Some right-to-death exponents want to argue for liberalized treatment termination on the basis of the recent abortion ruling of the Supreme Court. The court absolved itself of the obligation to protect the fetus, they argue, and by the same logic it has no special obligation to protect the remaining life of the dying. We should be on guard against the perverse tendency to stretch the abortion rhetoric to include the ending of life of hospitalized or nursing home patients. A wiser society would have been more resistant in the first place to the rhetoric of laissez faire abortion. For we now have on our hands ever-expanding claims to legitimize abortions of every kind, with over a million abortions per year currently being done, many against the citizenry's moral instincts and good moral judgment. Now may be the irretrievable time to offer intelligent resistance to right-to-death rhetoric, however idealistic it may sound. For all our historical examples of legalized mercy killing teach us that the beginnings were always small, and then only with collusions between physicians and policymakers, they grew into immense abuses.

"There is considerable question whether society wants to allow disposal of life to hinge on criteria such as 'meaningfulness,'" says jurist Norman Cantor, "or on the economic and emotional interest of persons other than the patient himself. . . . The authority (and disparate practices) assumed by some physicians in withholding care from newborn infants is indicative of the potential for abuse created when common medical practice becomes the legal norm with regard to salvation of life." If you are the parent of a genetically handicapped infant, you should know that your physician cannot withhold treatment unilaterally without risking criminal liability. The law gives natural guardianship to the parents. If the physician acts unilaterally to permit the infant to die, he exceeds his authority and may be subject to charges of wrongful death. The courts' inclinations have been toward imposing a professional duty favoring the infant's life. "Even if the parents assent to permitting a defective infant to die," writes Cantor, "the physician may not be able to avert criminal responsibility. The parents' conduct arguably constitutes criminal neglect. . . . The physician would also be violating mandatory reporting laws which exist in many states and which punish physicians for failure to report child neglect."

This is perhaps the best point at which to express a serious reservation about the social and legal consequences of the *Quinlan* ruling. For the court, in attempting to provide a solution to the family's dilemma, actually acted so as potentially to jeopardize the lives of many institutionalized retardates, senile, unconscious, and defenseless patients. A good judicial ruling should reduce future litigations, but in my opinion the *Quinlan* ruling is likely to accelerate litigations instead of reduce them.

Why, I have been asked, do I consider the ruling perilous? Because thousands of incompetent persons whose lives previously were clearly protected by law are now unclearly or dubiously protected. For what is to prevent a family from "doctor shopping" or even "hospital shopping" for a medical center lenient on treatment termination? What if the gravely ill patient is heavily insured? What if the family is not well-intentioned? What if a child is an institutionalized retardate, a burden on the family's mind, and suddenly is placed on life support with a serious illness? What is to prevent the family from asking for termination?

Many wrongful deaths are likely to occur unless this ruling is carefully constricted in its interpretation. The *Quinlan* ruling says to such families: You are immune from any liability if you get the approval of any one physician and an ethics committee of his hospital. What is to prevent abuses coming from this? Isn't it predictable that certain hospitals will become "euthanasia mills," just as some have become "abortion mills"? Just as a small percentage of hospitals have found it financially rewarding to develop an abortion clientele, why shouldn't we expect some to develop and accumulate by reputation a "treatment termination" clientele?

A Growing Movement? We have been discussing the dangers of a "wedge" forming and widening so as to weaken the "sanctity of life" principle. There is a consequent peril, however, that we overreact to the threat of the wedge and thus give it more importance than it actually has. Our society is probably not as far gone as the alarmists claim, and not likely to become so.

Some balance is needed. For our society is searching for reasonable criteria for treatment termination in irreversible cases. We cannot respond with a simple vitalism that says never under any conditions terminate. And yet does not even the notion of "criteria for treatment termination" constitute the thin edge of the wedge? Hardly. For the best defense against the wedge is not an absolutely rigid, purist idealism or vitalistic simplism, but rather reasoned criteria, carefully self-limiting, cautious and not subject to ever-expanding generalizations. A rigid vitalism may inadvertently encourage the wedge further, since some cases of treatment termination are, as we have shown, legitimate. The criteria presented in this chapter, we believe, will offer resistance to the wedge rather than a sell-out accommodation to it.

The wedge theory, like many social prediction theories, is subject to exaggeration itself. For it tends thoughtlessly to play into the hands of its opponents, the mercy-death activists who are by predisposition convinced that there exists a vital, "growing movement" in Western democracies to relax termination constraints generally. The actual record shows precisely the opposite. For virtually every legislative attempt to shift the interpretation of the equal protection clause in the direction of liberalized mercy deaths has failed.

The record:

1936 A bill was introduced in the House of Lords to legalize voluntary "easy death." After much public debate, defeated.

1938 A bill was introduced in the Nebraska legislature which would have allowed seriously ill persons to apply for permission for a "merciful death." Defeated.
Same bill introduced into the New York legislature. Failed.

1940 Euthanasia condemned by Pope Pius XII.

1946 A committee of 1,776 physicians petitioned the New York legislature for voluntary euthanasia. Defeated in 1947.

1950 The Church of England condemned euthanasia. Parliament again rejected voluntary mercy death.

1952 The General Convention of the Episcopal Church in America went on record as opposing the legalizing of euthanasia "under any circumstances whatsoever." The United Nations received a joint petition of English and American doctors, clergy, scientists to amend the Declaration of Human Rights to include voluntary merciful death. Tabled.

1957 The New Jersey legislature received a petition from 166 physicians to allow voluntary mercy death. Failed. Pope Pius XII discussed the withholding of extraordinary treatment, but again condemned all forms of euthanasia.

1968 Florida legislature began receiving annually and defeating annually Dr. Sackett's proposed "death with dignity" bill.

1969 House of Lords again rejects euthanasia.

1973 The *Heston* case affirmed that the right to refuse life-

sustaining treatment on religious grounds could not be
supported on constitutional grounds.

Since then numerous bills have been introduced in legislatures
of many states proposing liberalized mercy death, or as the Mon-
tana Constitutional Convention urged, to "allow every citizen to
choose the manner in which he dies," but all thus far have failed
to gain legislative acceptance.

Among the court's key findings in the landmark *Quinlan* case
(1976) was a firm rejection of the implication that its action
constituted "euthanasia." Quoting Bishop Casey it stated that
"authority to terminate a medical procedure characterized as
'an extraordinary means of treatment' would not involve euthanasia." For "medical science is not authorized to directly cause
death."

The (1976) California and similar statutes, which are attempting to legitimize the "living will" idea, have carefully
avoided extending their sanctions to any act of involuntary treatment termination, where patient consent is unknown.

So on what basis has the "growing movement" fantasy been
generated? Largely as a figment of journalists' imaginations. The
press wants a story and knows that dramatic or sentimental
versions of easy-death arguments are emotively appealing. But the
legislatures have little interest in changing our equal-protection
tradition, and considerable resistance when changes are proposed.

This chapter's concluding guideline: *The record shows that
there is no overwhelming or growing movement to condone
merciful death either as standard medical practice or by legal
sanction. A deepened historical awareness will prevent us from
being so easily deceived by those who view "easy death" as the
"next liberation" in the tradition of laissez faire abortion.*

American courts have never agreed with the theories of a few
commentators that a broad constitutional right to death can be
derived from the right to privacy or restrictions against cruel and
unusual punishment. The right to life is explicitly stated in the

Fifth and Fourteenth Amendments. So it is hardly surprising that there are no explicit constitutional guarantees arguing for a right to death, either in the case of suicide or merciful death. In fact, if the state fails reasonably to protect a defenseless patient from an action deliberately intending to cause death, relatives or advocates could ask for redress from the state for its failure to supply equal protection under law. Claims for a broadly construed constitutional "right to death" constitute essentially a rhetoric searching for legitimation of a social policy that in its details is likely to continue to be rejected by American courts and public opinion.

3. RESPECT FOR LIFE
AND THE ACCEPTANCE
OF DEATH

Patiently we have threaded our way through the maze of questions focusing on *who* is to give informed consent to treatment termination in irreversible illness (chapter 1), and *how* we are to weigh the various factors that often impinge on a decision to extend or end life (chapter 2).

A major exercise in moral reflection lies yet ahead of us, however. For we are also concerned to place the question of treatment termination in its appropriate philosophical, ethical, and religious context. If we fail here, we fail to grasp the question in its depth as a profound dilemma of the human spirit.

In pursuit of this aim, this chapter asks why Jewish and Christian theology does not affirm an absolute right to death; why Christianity views "death with dignity" in a different way than does secular hedonism; and why the biblical view of providence views life as meaningful, even amid suffering and death, precisely at those points that appear to us to be meaningless. Here we find ourselves set in a sea of profound and perennial questions of religious truth: What is uniquely to be learned from the situation of facing death, whether our own or another's? How does God's own suffering and death transform our understanding of our suffering and death? Why is the acceptance of death a form of the acceptance of life? At the center of all these questions, in my mind, is the pivotal religious issue underneath all our other debates: whether relief of suffering is a greater value than life itself.

Respect for Life in the Western Religious Tradition. Does a Judeo-Christian view of treatment termination differ in substance from the legal and medical reasoning that we have sought to understand in the previous chapters? Does it place the question of respect for life and acceptance of death in a larger frame of reference, in fact a universal-historical context which distinguishes it from even a wise and sensitive secular view?

Yes. For in this religious tradition, which has so profoundly influenced both medical and legal practice, and yet which is not reducible to them, life is beheld and celebrated as the gift of God. It is in the ecstasy of that awesome awareness that Jewish and Christian religious thought enters the debate, and in a sense, intensifies the dilemmas of treatment termination. For it is unwilling ever to allow us to see life in instrumental or use-oriented terms. Every particular human life is unique, incalculably valuable, addressed with its special calling and destiny, and is properly understood only in the context of the divine gift, claim, and purpose.

My aim in this chapter is to set forth in its main outlines some of the major ways in which the Western religious tradition transmutes the questions of premortem ethics, and requires that they be seen in a surprisingly different context than that which prevails in modern secular hedonism.

However wretched at times, life is not something to be disposed of arbitrarily by human hands (Job 2:9–12). God alone is the author of life, and no human being has the right to end the life of another (Exod. 23:7). According to Scripture, "No one has power to retain the spirit, or authority over the day of death" (Eccles. 8:8).

If the right to life is inalienable, and if life is God's precious gift, then it cannot lawfully be renounced, according to this tradition, even by the lucid individual with his deliberate consent. For according to Jewish and Christian teaching, the individual does not have absolute right to self-determination over even his own bodily life, much less the life of another. Life is not given merely for pleasure to be discarded when pain comes, but rather for the deepening of the human spirit and for growth in responsiveness to God's grace even and precisely amid suffering when regrettably it comes. Human freedom has much to learn about its own source and ground precisely through struggling through its own specific limitations, not the least of which are suffering and death.

Shallow hedonism has never learned what faith in God knows: that it is not suffering itself that is the enemy of human freedom and dignity but rather poor and thoughtless responses to suffering. The only thing hedonism has learned about suffering is that it is to be avoided. It takes it for granted that death is preferable to irreversible suffering.

Not so with faith in God, which has learned that suffering is never to be sought, but when it comes, as it inevitably comes to serious human existence, God's special grace is present in its limitations. Faith witnesses to having learned something about its radical dependence upon God through suffering—knowledge which it doubts could have been gained without suffering. So even suffering, according to Jeremiah and Augustine and Luther, is perceived by faith as a significant part of God's providential purpose in the nurture of human character toward ever-fuller responsiveness to the gifts and possibilities of life, even in the face of death.

Guideline thirty two: *There is nothing in Western religious teaching that suggests that we should go around looking for pain, or fail to relieve pain; but when suffering comes we learn, as Paul learned, "My grace is sufficient for you, for my power is made perfect in weakness"* (2 Cor. 12:9). Christian teaching affirms the use of medical science to relieve pain, but it does not understand pain as worse than taking another's life, or the relief of suffering as a self-evidently higher value than life itself. For Christians know that it is precisely through the struggle with our human limitations that we learn something distinctive about the grace and mercy of God, who himself was willing to suffer for us on the cross.

Do You Have a Right to Death? Why is it that the Protestant, Catholic, and Jewish traditions all assert that we have a right to life, but not an absolute right to death? Life is already a gift, and therefore we have an implicit right to it and a responsibility to receive it. Death will someday come, but we do not have an arbitrary right to choose the time and circumstances of our dying.

It is as if God is the rightful owner and provider of our life, but it is loaned to us on the assumption that we will exercise good stewardship over it during this fleeting span of moments, and then return it to God. It is in this sense that Augustine viewed the taking of life, either of oneself or another, as an injustice not only to oneself or the other, but to God. Ending a life is an offense against the source and ground of life on the simple assumption that it is an unparalleled gift, eminently worthy of being received, even under harsh and challenging adversities. It is an offense to the Creator to give it back thanklessly or to waste it prodigally.

Scripture understands death, therefore, as a return: "The dust returns to the earth as it was; and the spirit returns to God who gave it" (Eccles. 12:7). God the Creator, as sovereign and legitimate authority over all life and creation, alone has authority to give and take away life (Job 1:21).

If we hold life only temporarily as a trust, we may use it, receive it, celebrate it, and prolong it, but we may not destroy it at will. Guideline thirty-three: *The only circumstance under which life may be justly taken, in classical Jewish and Christian ethics, is in defensive resistance to an unjust aggressor against an indi-*

vidual or the common good. For in extreme or emergency circumstances, such as a just defensive war or personal self-defense, one may be required to take another's life in order to defend the common good, to protect another's life or one's own.

The Central Dilemma. This leads us to the central ethical dilemma: When relief of suffering competes with the value of life itself, should life itself be judged the higher value?

There is no doubt that relief of suffering is a profound demand upon moral consciousness. It is an expression of compassion and mercy.

But traditional Western law, medicine and morality have never been willing to concede that the relief of suffering is unambiguously a greater value than life itself, for several reasons:

Life is the basis for all other human goods. No good can be done unless the doer is alive. Death, in its elementary sense, means the loss of any capacity to experience or transmit any realizable good. There is no human value conceivable unless human life is presupposed. Human life is therefore the precondition of all possible human values, including merciful relief of suffering.

Furthermore, suffering does not defeat life's goodness. Surely the troubles of Israel, the book of Job, the story of Jesus, Paul's thorn in the flesh, the Talmud, the confessions of Augustine, the poetry of Milton, the parables of Kierkegaard, the plays of O'Neill and the psychology of Frankl all teach us that. For in them we see both the depths of suffering, yet with an enhanced and deepened awareness of the value of life amid suffering. Whatever its tragic limitations, the human spirit at its best affirms the goodness of life amid the severest limitations as the necessary condition of all potential and actual values we can conceive.

Suppose the act of relieving suffering were universally and consistently regarded as of higher moral worth than the act of preserving life? What kind of society would result and how would we act? It would then be accepted practice to assist persons in dying who are experiencing any intense suffering. The aiding and abetting of suicide would be a duty rather than an illegal act. If a person were experiencing mental anguish after the breakup of a loving relationship and begged you to help him end his life, it would be your duty to help relieve his suffering. But we know this is foolish. No society condones such behavior, because ordinary moral awareness grasps this fundamental insight: Life is of incomparable value, since it is the precondition of all values. It is on a wholly different plane, morally speaking, than is the relief of suffering, which itself is in the service of life. When relief of suffering enters the service of death, its moral credentials are put severely into question. The biblical witness sharpens this contrast in a way that suggests our next guideline: *Since life is God's gift, and therefore of incalculable value, and since suffering is properly to be seen always and only within the context of divine providence, there is no definable point at which Jewish and Christian consciousness can say that the value of relieving suffering becomes greater than the value of life itself.*

But, it may be objected, aren't there some instances where suffering becomes so great and hopeless that life loses all potential value? Haven't we already said, for example, that if a person has lost all cognitive capacity and is near death, that is sufficient reason to terminate new initiatives in treatment, and doesn't that imply that the relief of that suffering is a greater and preferable value than life in its bare noncognitive form? Not exactly. For noncognitive life cannot be relieved of suffering since it does not in the strict sense suffer, if suffering is dependent upon consciousness and cognition.

A rigorous Christian ethic argues that there is never any point in the Christian's experience of life where the intensity of suffering finally and totally negates the value of life itself. For Christians are given a specific promise by the God who has chosen to live (and if necessary suffer) human life with us. It is that "God is faithful, and he will not let you be tested beyond your strength"

(1 Cor. 10:13). The Christian believer trusts that promise. That is why, in our schema, the degree of discomfort is not a primary indicator of treatment termination although it indeed is a secondary consideration and a meaningful supplement to the constellation of primary indicators.

Is life by this reasoning an absolute value? No. Life is a derived value, derived as are all finite values from their Creator. Life's goodness is not greater than the source and end of life. Life's value is relative to the giver of life, but greater than all things that do not have life. And of all forms of created life known to us, the human personality, with love, imagination, conscience, and reason, is the most highly valued form of life we know, because it is created in the image of God.

When is Life Meaningless? Is life only meaningful at those times we pronounce it meaningful? Guideline thirty-five: *The biblical understanding of providence views life as meaningful within God's frame of reference every moment, regardless of whether we perceive its meaning, and even when we are completely convinced that it is meaningless.* This is exactly what faith in providence asserts: that the unfolding of time and history is meaningful precisely in those moments that seem totally meaningless. It is one of the most outrageous pretensions of modern individualism to say that something can only be meaningful if I experience it as such.

The pleasure principle says when life is not good, give it up. Why not? When it involves more pain than pleasure, take an exit, and even help others take their exit. This view stands in direct opposition to the understanding that life is God's gift for responsible stewardship of time-limited life and breath.

Advocates of the pleasure principle do not often understand that suffering in spirit is the distinctive privilege of the human personality, fitted as it is with imagination, conscience, reason, and hope. Animal and plant life cannot as fully share this potential because the capacity for complex acts of imagination and responsibility is not as fully given. It is just that capacity for the internal conflict of body and conscience that characterizes human existence over against the nonhuman creation. It is precisely the capacity for anxiety and guilt (which inevitably accompanies freedom), that signals the unexcelled privilege of human consciousness. So to attempt to escape, as many "humanists" do, the realities of body-spirit suffering is in effect to escape our deeper humanity. For, as we should have been well taught by Hillel, Augustine, or Aquinas as well as Calvin and Kierkegaard, human existence is rooted in nature, yet capable of self-transcendence. To live life deeply is to experience the tension which characterizes human existence as both finite and free, both causally determined yet capable of self-determination, both body and spirit. To escape this tension and suffering is an escape from freedom.

The other side of a pure hedonism which says that pleasure is life's sole good is a frenetic, compulsive avoidance of anything that looks like pain, discomfort, or inconvenience. When hedonism describes one's duty merely as the fulfilling of the pleasure-seeking instincts, it implicitly also views the avoidance of discomfort as a duty.

But anyone who meets life in its depths knows that suffering need not defeat us. It can be our greatest challenge. Christian faith has no thought of making the value of life as God's gift dependent upon the amount of suffering we experience. It is through Israel's struggles, Jesus' death and resurrection that we learn that God's grace is present amid suffering to call us into new life.

The Christian lives and dies daily with Christ. This is a central insight of the Christian life. Yet it is probably meaningful only to those who have risked acting upon it experientially. So the written page is an inadequate means of communicating the gospel of resurrection. It is more persuasively stated in the presence of one who is living the resurrected life, whose life is hid with God in Christ, who experiences daily his baptism, his dying and living with Christ.

The Paradox of Limitation. Christian wisdom has historically had a decisive interest in the decisions surrounding death. It may seem incongruous to look upon impending death as a potential means of spiritual regeneration. It is from a deep stratum of the biblical tradition, however, that we draw our thirty-sixth guideline: *There are profound learning possibilities offered in the situation of facing death, one's own or another's, that are not available in ordinary human experience.*

Death may become an extraordinary source of the revelation of life's meaning and of the illumination of the human condition. Christian pastoral care does not want the seriously ill person or his loved ones to miss the opportunities for expanded religious vision and insight that may be uniquely offered in the confrontation with death. This hope is pressed without yielding to an ascetic preoccupation with death or hunger for suffering. Afflictions do not have in themselves redemptive efficacy. "God does not will everything that happens," writes Aulen, "but he does will something in everything that happens."

Some growth-producing insights are grasped only through poverty. Some knowledge is gained only through the hazards of risk, vulnerability, and struggle. Some wisdom comes only through street-smart or the school of hard knocks. These insights simply may not be available amid comfortable existence. It is for the same reason that certain spiritual insights grow only in the context of difficulty, limitation, and ultimately in the confrontation with death. They are not achieved in times of health, invulnerability, ecstasy, or satisfaction.

Hindrances and obstacles challenge our best capacities. Jeremiah wrote his prophecies in deep anguish of spirit. Paul wrote several of his letters from prisons and amid great physical risk and hardship. Dante produced his greatest work, *The Divine*

Comedy, in poverty and exile. John Bunyan wrote *Pilgrim's Progress* in a cramped and dirty jail cell. Martin Luther King, Jr. wrote his most moving essay, "Letter from a Birmingham Jail," amid the most incredible frustrations. It is not accidental that these great spiritual writings were produced under conditions of limitation. For it is only when the human spirit is challenged to suffer redemptively that its greatest potential is elicited.

Please do not misread me: it is not directly to suffering, sickness, and imprisonment that we owe these achievements, but to the particular challenge the human spirit experiences in response to trial, limitation, and suffering.

I conclude that anyone who has never known limitation and suffering probably has not experienced his full human potential. Some of the greatest works of art have been accomplished by persons trapped in the severest constrictions. Beethoven wrote his greatest works under the burden of an increasing deafness that so seriously interfered with his art that he almost put an end to his life. Milton's greatest literary achievements were written after he had become blind. Pope, Schiller, and Cooper did much of their literary work amid chronic illnesses; so did Keats and Sir Walter Scott. Elizabeth Barrett Browning was curiously aware that as her bodily strength decreased, her intellectual and poetic powers seemed to increase. This is the spiritual paradox of limitation. Affliction challenges spiritual growth.

What does suffering do for us that pleasure cannot do? To begin with, it helps us to experience the capacity to endure that we may never have thought we had. As long as our patience and endurance remains untested, we are forever ignorant of our specific human potential. We are unacquainted with our will to live, the strength of our patience, and our capacity to survive under harsh or stultifying conditions.

It is not surprising, in the light of the experience of Jesus, that Christian faith should understand suffering and affliction as a schoolmaster to bring us to the truth. This is consistent with Israel's experience of God in the Old Testament. In response to the faithlessness of Israel, the Lord declared through his prophet Hosea: "Therefore I will hedge up her way with thorns; and I will build a wall against her, so that she cannot find her paths." All these difficulties had the educative and redemptive purpose of bringing Israel back to covenant faithfulness.

It is easy to thank God for our obvious blessings, but it takes much keener spiritual perception to thank God for those challenges that come to us in the form of loss and limitation. Yet we know that these troublesome experiences call forth our best spiritual energies. It was in taking up his cross that Jesus supremely expressed his faithfulness. It is only in taking up our cross that we participate in Jesus' ministry.

The old homiletic metaphors still ring true: The stars are brightest in the heart of darkness. The diamond is able to gleam only if it is cut and polished. The rainbow does not appear except amid the showers. It is only when the oyster is wounded by a grain of irritating sand that it begins to develop a pearl.

This does not mean that troubles are good or inevitably growth producing. Understood faithfully from within the frame of reference of God's instructive providence, afflictions can do us good. Bitterly and cynically understood, they can do us harm.

God's Suffering and Ours. Life is given only under the specific limits of birth and death. For Christians this becomes most dramatically portrayed for us in God's own engagement in human history. For according to the New Testament, God meets us not in the form of an immortal, invulnerable deity of the Greek mythical tradition, but rather in the form of a person who is born—born! Into this human life with its specific limitations. In a manger! No room in the inn.

Guideline thirty-seven: *The God by whom Christian worship has been met is one who engages in this human history under the same conditions we as human beings know, including pain, limitation, and loss.* The good news is the story of God's own determination deeply to experience the conditions of human life,

Respect for Life and the Acceptance of Death   79

suffering, and death, so as to participate fully in our human condition.

It is precisely in the light of this story that we enter into the realm of end-care decision making. This is the history that bears final, illuminating significance for our decisions. Christian faith reasons by analogy: The source and ground of life has known suffering and death. In meeting Jesus we meet one who teaches us to trust the giver and end of all things as a good father, even amid the circumstances of our own death. In Jesus' companionship, we learn to say with Job, "Though he slay me, yet will I trust him."

It is in the light of Jesus' confrontation with death that we experience our own confrontations with death. Our sense of radical loss is viewed in the light of God's own radical loss. The triune God knows and understands our death and the death of those we love. God the Parent has experienced the death of his own child.

It was out of a specific confrontation with a specific death that the Christian message was born. Out of the tomb the resurrected church emerged. Out of the blood of the martyrs the seeds of the church were planted. Meeting death is no stranger to Christian trust in God. Christian faith celebrates the One who walks this way with us. Even though it involves the sorrow of separation, it also hopes confidently in return, resurrection, and renewal.

"Lord Jesus, you know what pain is like," wrote William Barclay. "You know the torture of the scourge upon your back, the sting of the thorns upon your brow, the agony of the nails in your hands. You know what I'm going through just now. Help me to bear my pain gallantly, cheerfully and patiently, and help me to remember that I will never be tried above what I am able to bear, and that you are with me, even in this valley of the deep dark shadow."

Rather than controlling the time and place and means of ending our lives, most of us will face instead the profounder task of how we are to live until we die, leaving the mode and means of death to powers and determinations beyond our own. Although treatment may be terminated, as we have shown, in some highly deteriorated instances, this is our more frequent moral challenge in terminal care: living within the limits of remaining life, rather than living with our own decision to authorize death.

Courageous Trust. The courage that lives out of communion with Christ is more than humanistic courage or self-control. It is a form of confidence grounded in God's providential care, made known through a history of God's self-disclosure amid God's passionate involvement in the human condition. It is not a grave, submissive, passionless, stoic endurance, but a joyful responsive willingness to trust a loving Parent even amid life's challenges and difficulties. Guideline thirty-eight: *The whole history of God's grace in human life demonstrates to us that God is ready to be our companion amid hazardous choices.*

Anyone who is fixated solely upon preserving his physical life loses his true self. "Remember Lot's wife," warned Jesus. "Whoever seeks to gain his life will lose it, but whoever loses his life will preserve it" (Luke 17:32–33).

"None of us lives to himself," writes Paul, "and none of us dies to himself. If we live, we live to the Lord, and if we die, we die to the Lord; so then, whether we live or whether we die, we are the Lord's. For to this end Christ died and lived again, that he might be Lord both of the dead and of the living" (Rom. 14:7–9).

Some think the family is under unprecedented challenge today. But in crucial moments we see the hidden strength of the contemporary family revealed. This often happens most clearly when one of its members is seriously ill or facing some awesome difficulty. Then we learn who cares. Toynbee thought that we never learn the strength of a civilization until we see it tested. So it is with the family. Until its will to live is tested, its hidden spiritual resources may lie dormant. Then each member of the family draws strength from the other. Often exceptional spiritual strength is drawn from one member of the family whose life is deeply rooted in faith in God amid the realities of life.

You may have prayed that your companion recover. The tide of suffering may not have been stemmed. You may have wept for your companion and felt helpless to relieve the pain. It saddens you to see this valued person losing ground, facing mounting difficulties, struggling without the possibility of winning. All this may raise for you the most profound questions about the fundamental justice of the conditions under which God allows our lives to proceed and finally end.

In these dark moments of doubt and internal struggle, keep in mind that you are surrounded by love. Many people care. There is a community of people praying that your spirit will be strengthened and your conscience wisely instructed. There is a living community of prayer participating in your struggle, praying for your courage and clarity of vision. You are not alone as you walk through the valley of the shadow of death.

If you think you are alone, meditate for a moment on the people you know who care about what happens to your stricken companion. Let them come to mind one by one, and pass before you in consciousness. Then with these companions stand before God and ask for direction. Pray for right judgment. You are not likely to make mistaken judgments when God's guidance has earnestly been sought.

"No wonder we do not lose heart!" exclaimed Paul. "Though our outward humanity is in decay, yet day by day we are inwardly renewed. Our troubles are slight and short-lived; and their outcome an eternal glory which outweighs them far. Meanwhile our eyes are fixed, not on the things that are seen, but on the things that are unseen: for what is seen passes away; what is unseen is eternal. For we know that if the earthly frame that houses us today should be demolished, we possess a building which God has provided—a house not made by human hands, eternal, and in heaven. In this present body we do indeed groan; we yearn to have our heavenly habitation put on over this one—in the hope that, being thus clothed, we shall not find ourselves naked. . . . Therefore we never cease to be confident" (2 Cor. 4:16–5:6).

Suffering Without Shame. Modernity has made suffering itself an unsufferable indignity. But note carefully the calm, patient language of Scripture, hammered out of the experience of Israel and the early Christian community: "Whom the Lord loves, he chastens" (Rev. 3:19). "Behold, I have refined you, but not like silver: I have tried you in the furnace of affliction" (Isa. 48:10). "This is cause for great joy, even though now you smart for a little while, if need be, under trials of many kinds. Even gold passes through the assayer's fire, and more precious than perishable gold is faith which has stood the test. These trials come so that your faith may prove itself worthy" (1 Pet. 1:6, 7). "My son, do not despise the Lord's discipline, or be weary of his reproof, for the Lord reproves him whom he loves, as a father the son in whom he delights" (Prov. 3:11, 12).

Suffering? "You must endure it as a discipline: God is treating you as sons. Can anyone be a son, who is not disciplined by his father? If you escape the discipline in which all sons share, you must be bastards and no true sons. Again, we paid due respect to the earthly fathers who disciplined us; should we not submit even more readily to our spiritual Father, and so attain life? They disciplined us for this short life according to their lights; but he does so for our true welfare, so that we may share his holiness. Discipline, no doubt, is never pleasant; at the time it seems painful, but in the end it yields for those who have been trained by it the peaceful harvest of an honest life. Come, then, stiffen your drooping arms and shaking knees, and keep your steps from wavering. Then the disabled limb will not be put out of joint, but regain its former powers" (Heb. 12:5–13).

Our thirty-ninth guideline follows: *Far from being an obscenity, crossbearing or redemptive suffering is the mark of the Christian life:* "Never be ashamed of your testimony to our Lord," Paul writes Timothy, "nor of me his prisoner, but take your share of suffering for the sake of the gospel" (2 Tim. 1:8). "Though it is true at this moment that I am suffering on behalf of you who have heard the gospel, yet I am far from sorry about it. Indeed, I am glad, because it gives me a chance to complete in my own sufferings something of the untold pains which Christ suffers on behalf of his body, the church" (Col. 1:24).

Without morbidity, biblical faith celebrates that our afflictions are purposeful, within God's purposes, just as are our achievements: "In the day of prosperity be joyful, and in the day of adversity consider; God has made the one as well as the other" (Eccles. 7:14). The Apostles declared that they rejoiced even in their present sufferings "because we know that suffering trains us to endure, and endurance brings proof that we have stood the test, and this proof is the ground of hope" (Rom. 5:5).

The Compulsive Need to Control. It is seldom our business to take into our own hands a decision about when and how to die. That may be a "noble idea" of Roman stoic philosophy, but it goes against the grain of everything the Jewish and Christian tradition knows about life as God's gift, and about the receiving of life under the specific limitations which God's providence has allotted us.

Needing to select our time to die (as distinguished from legitimate treatment termination under previously stated guidelines) is an expression of our inordinate hunger to control, our arrogance in compulsively longing to influence and determine the conditions of our existence. This is an evidence of the *hubris*, or pride, which Greek tragedy considered the major cause of human misery. When we need to control most or all of the conditions of our own death, we are too desperately hungry for a power and authority that does not properly belong to us. When we possessively want to direct in detail when and how our own lives should end, this is to arrogate to ourselves an artificial mastery over our destinies that is in one sense comic, but in a larger sense tragically heroic.

But if it is wrong to shorten life, then is it not equally wrong to lengthen life? This perplexity was pondered by David Hume who in 1777 argued that if our shortening lives interferes with providence, then all medical care also interferes with providence by lengthening life. The classical answer is that if life is good, then to shorten it is evil, but to lengthen it is good. It is only when life loses all possibility for actualizing any of its essential goodness that treatment termination becomes arguable.

Only the most constricted and unimaginative view of providence concludes that all medical care should be refused in order to let natural diseases "providentially" have their way. For we are also given by providence a prudential intelligence to use creatively in sustaining life, and a natural instinct for self-preservation.

Providence also implants within us, however, an abhorrence of suffering and a determination to avoid pain, especially unnecessary pain. Medical care that merely prolongs hopeless suffering seems to frustrate that natural inclination to avoid pain. Medical care that ends life deliberately on behalf of the relief of suffering, however, facilitates the avoidance of pain only by the extreme means of ending life itself.

I have tried in chapter 2 not to dodge the tough issue of specifically stating what situations warrant treatment termination. It is evident, however, that these situations are rare. In most premortem situations we will find ourselves mercifully preserving life and working to protect even the sharply limited remaining capacities to breathe, relate, smile, experience human relationships, think, and remember. Therefore *the deeper moral claim facing most companions during serious illness is not how or when to terminate life, but under the conditions of life's continuation, how are we to care well for the critically ill, how to understand our continuing responsibilities to our stricken covenant partners, and how we are to mature spiritually through these troubles.*

Dying with Dignity. Does a Judeo-Christian perspective on treatment termination, therefore, differ substantially from a wise and sensitive secular view? If the answer is yes, as I believe it is, then how does a well-instructed theology of premortem care probe greater depths than do court decisions, medical prognoses, and even moral analyses?

. The center of the answer, in my mind, lies in the extremely different ways we understand that ambiguous phrase "death with dignity." That phrase has been captured and propagated by a specific group of reformers who are seeking basic changes in social attitudes toward mercy death and treatment termination. The rhetoric of personal rights and self-determination has made their views seem appealing. In my library is a rather imposing shelf of their books (at least two dozen) which can be classified generally under the theme: The Right to Die. These authors (Heifetz, Mannes, Fletcher, et al.) represent the general viewpoint against which this discussion seeks to offer a modest alternative. The most evident weakness of that shelf of books is that it is pretentious in its program of reform, but has not thought carefully through the legal and medical consequences of its reform. The less evident but more profound weakness of that bookshelf is that it has too readily judged historical wisdom as irrelevant to the situation of irreversible illness, and has viewed traditional religious teachings on suffering, death, and providence as antiquated. This chapter has been trying to begin to redress that imbalance.

So this is admittedly a nonmainstream argument, an exercise in dissent from that popular literature on the "right to death." Most of that morose literature shares the scanty philosophical assumptions of secular humanism, the death-of-God speculators, and nineteenth-century utilitarianism. It knows nothing of Israel's hopes, Jesus' resurrection, or God's providence. Above all, the mainstream of popular literature is cynical about one of the key moral values bequeathed by thirty centuries of Western ethical experience: the sanctity of life.

My challenge is not oblique or evasive. The issues must be stated forthrightly: (1) Although most right-to-death advocates are curiously preoccupied with suffering, they do not express even a minimal awareness that suffering and loss could be a significant part of the divine intention as a challenge to the human potential and a special avenue of grace. (2) Although they are preoccupied with the rhetoric of freedom, they usually misunderstand freedom as if it could be separable from moral responsibility. (3) Although the right-to-death rhetoric talks a lot about the dangers of avoidance of death, it strikes me that it often colludes in another form of avoidance which may be even more dangerous—the avoidance of uncomfortable moral claims. In its anxious desire to avoid the inconveniences that death brings, it often avoids the concrete moral obligation of next of kin to care for the dying amid those inconveniences. In its inexpensive talk about the right to death, it sometimes forgets the responsibility to life. The prophets foretold a time of alienation when "death shall be chosen rather than life" (Jer. 8:3). Those who are asserting an absolute "right to die" in suicide and mercy death appear to be living out that prophecy in our own time.

In short, much of this popular morose literature is searching for an easier moral rationale than biblical faith can allow. Death seems to be an achievement. Relaxation of moral constraints against suicide and mercy killing are applauded as human "progress." The concept of progress itself is understood in the same inverted sense that those who argued for abortion thought it was an ennobling and progressive step in social history. Again we learn that far too much that is called progress is actually barbaric modernism, regressive reformism, dehumanizing humanism and uncaring "care."

Sometimes an author's intention is more clearly revealed by disclosing what he is struggling against. Although I have already presented several practical constructive proposals for change, I confess to at least four pet peeves: (1) the view that unrestricted "mercy death" is "the next liberation" (Mannes); (2) the use of the metaphor "persistent vegetative state," a phrase that easily becomes a linguistic means of rationalizing the treatment of human beings as vegetables; (3) legislative or judicial sanctions that

Respect for Life and the Acceptance of Death   87

would give guardians a broadly construable authority to judge some point at which the alleged "quality" of a sick person's life would warrant its discontinuance; and (4) the uncritical assertion of an absolute right to self-determination, as though the assertion of individual rights self-evidently overrides all other social and moral considerations.

Since right-to-death advocates take as their basic premise that irreversible suffering is an absolute evil, they focus microscopically on the horror of terminal disease and the inconveniences and indignities of the dying process. Traditional Jewish and Christian wisdom, however, has viewed the dying process from a boldly different angle of vision which illuminates and transmutes the meaning of the phrase "death with dignity." That phrase has been reduced regrettably to meaning merely "end it all soon." The biblical witness focuses surprisingly rather on gratefully living through the dying process with dignity rather than avoiding it. This brings us to guideline forty-one: *There is a particular quiet dignity present amid receptive acquiescence to the specific conditions of human existence which from time to time involve loss and limitation.* This is an unpretentious dignity often missed entirely by the pleasure-principle philosophy, a dignity that embraces the givenness of this life including suffering and death without seeking an easy or cheap escape, and which views the loss of human capacities as a challenge to the human spirit.

So this is, admittedly, a book with a "viewpoint" (different from most of its genre), yet I firmly believe that its viewpoint is centrist when viewed from the perspective of the general social and moral consensus in Western culture. This book does not include the usual biographical references because I am convinced that the major contributions to the debate on treatment termination are yet waiting to be made, but the authors who have most influenced me in my own struggle to see my way through these perplexities are all centrist writers: Ramsey, Kübler-Ross, Haering, Gustafson, Curran, Epstein, Dyck, McCormick, Thielicke, and Vaux.

Amid the general drift in our society toward the cheapening of the value of life, permissive abortion and the ethics of utility, Jewish and Christian ethics must look for end-care norms consistent with their historic self-understanding. Against current momentum they must offer some wise correctives. Most urgently this will take the form of a firm determination to protect those whose lives are least protected—I am referring especially to infants who are judged by guardians to be defective, worthless or subpersonal, and to the terminally ill who are thought to have little usefulness to society amid the "meaningless" process of dying.

We are now in a cultural milieu which is trigger-ready to devalue life because of the population explosion, the world food crisis, lifeboat ethics and the triage mentality. This is a momentum some feel is too powerful to resist. It will be resisted by those firmly committed to the Jewish and Christian understanding of human personhood as image of God.

CONCLUSION

Death comes to us all. We are never fully prepared for it. But it is a familiar possibility. There is a sense in which one begins to confront the possibility of dying at birth. All life is lived, as Heidegger said, "toward death." Faced with serious illness, we know this immediately.

Death does its worst by taking what is best, life, in its own way and time. Yet death is never greater than the source and end of life. The suffering by which we may have to enter the threshold of death is never greater than the ground and giver of life. Death gives us the unique opportunity to exercise our trust in the One who gives us life, who showed his love for us by engaging fully in the conditions of human existence, by his death and resurrection.

Kierkegaard was ecstatic with joy over the simple thought that suffering necessarily must end, since human bodily existence is finite, yet since human spiritual existence is eternal it necessarily transcends this limited time-bound sphere of suffering. While human time is limited, God's time is unlimited. "For a thousand years in thy sight are but as yesterday when it is past, and as a watch in the night" (Ps. 90:4).

The Bible is keenly aware of the fragility of human life. "Our years come to an end like a sigh," says the Psalmist. "The years of our life are threescore and ten, or even by reason of strength fourscore. . . . They are soon gone, and we fly away. . . . So teach us to number our days that we may get a heart of wisdom" (Ps. 90:9–12). "Do not boast about tomorrow," says the Proverb, "for you do not know what a day may bring forth" (Prov. 27:1).

Although you may stand in the presence of impending death, keep in mind that you are there because of life. You are trying to do justice and charity amid approaching death to one whose life you affirm and value. You are there in that spot because you hold this particular life to be inestimably valuable. Do not become so preoccupied with death that you fail to see the particular value and beauty of the remaining life.

Unexpectedly, premortem care faces us with the opportunity to deepen our reverence for life. How precious life really is. How fragile and vulnerable it is to destruction, corruption, and death. How much we actually do live by faith in our possible, and not yet actual futures. How impossible it is for us finally to secure our mortal existence. How beyond our power it is to pretend that we control the conditions of life.

Confronting death teaches us to receive life as unmerited gift. New forms of consciousness are then made possible which were unimaginable before, without death as companion. The death-confronting moment may be the most realistic basis upon which one learns that dying is a God-given part of the offer of life, and that faith in God permits one to give up trusting in one's own achievements.

The life-death confrontation gives us moderns an opportunity to learn something of what the medieval writers called *ars moriendi*, the art of dying well. This is an art that must be learned long before death, of course. In fact, properly speaking, it was for the medieval mind an education that goes on throughout the whole of one's life, to prepare for the last hour.

Many occasions confront us with losses similar to death. When we have to face limitations, sometimes abruptly and unexpectedly, sometimes slowly and drawn out, these may be like "partial deaths" in the sense that they involve potential losses that are irrecoverable. Moving away from old friends in my home state was to me something like dying. In losing a competition recently I felt a small part of myself die. Being rejected by a good friend felt something like dying. I still grieve over some lost relationships with persons with whom I cannot now communicate.

So it seems with many human experiences. Our concluding guideline: *Each time we meet unknown limitations we are in a sense preparing ourselves for the ultimate limitation.* Each one of these encounters has a potential for teaching us the acquiescent virtues, patient tolerance of the limitations of human existence, acceptance of the conditions of life under which God places all creatures. Human experiencing is bounded by such limits. We are thus given many opportunities to prepare our spirits for our own dying and the death of those we love.

The bonds of intimacy are deepened through confronting affliction together. Two persons who are learning to trust each other must face limitations together in order to test and reaffirm their mutual trustability. It is only when the bonding has been challenged by hard days as well as easy ones that it becomes secured. Such persons have richer companionships than those whose interaction is based solely on receiving happiness.

To our surprise we may find that our capacity to empathize, to enter imaginatively into the experiencing process of others, is incredibly enriched through our struggle with the approaching death of one we love. For empathy can only grow as our capacity to sense the contours of others' experience grows. And since death is an inexorable aspect of every human being's future experience, our encounter with the death of another for whom we care may illuminate that vulnerable and time-bound aspect of all human experiencing. Thus, without limitation and loss, the compassionate virtues would all be immobilized. And without death, as Frankl said, we would forever be tempted to postpone acts of responsible freedom, since everything could be delayed indefinitely. Ironically, it is from death that human freedom receives its most powerful vindication.